GATES

OF

DANNEMORA

BY JOHN L. BONN

GATES OF DANNEMORA
HOUSE ON THE SANDS
AND DOWN THE DAYS
SO FALLS THE ELM TREE

GATES
OF
DANNEMORA

DOUBLEDAY & COMPANY, INC., GARDEN CITY, N.Y., 1951

BY JOHN L. BONN

FOREWORD

This book needs no dedication. Of itself, it is dedicated to Father Hyland and to the real men whose names I have not used and whose identities I have disguised. But I have seen and talked to them. I have read them their portions of this manuscript. And I count as close friends those who have learned from their priest the meaning of true redemption.

Its purpose is positive. It is a reminder that conviction and detention are not synonyms for correction. It may even assert that the convicted are still alive, and that they are human beings. It claims the possibility of contrition and amendment. Perhaps more.

I know what Father Hyland would like me to say, so I quote him: "This book presents a true story of a group of individuals about whom you probably know very little. Yet you or I might easily have become part of this group. The gulf which separates us and them is not nearly so impassable as some of us like to suppose."

For the rest, I have tried to tell about him. Let it speak for itself.

I cannot stop, however, without a word of thanks to Father W. Coleman Nevils, S. J., of *America,* for introducing me to some of the most compelling experiences of my life; or to Mr. John C. Rogan of the Republic Book Company for sharing them with me and for invaluable assistance in preparing this manuscript. And I thank God for having been, with my friends, many times now, in the Church of the Good Thief, behind the Gates of Dannemora.

J.L.B.

BOOK
ONE:
SIBERIA

CHAPTER ONE

It was not a new experience for him to look in through these foot-squared barred windows of the prison gates. He had done it often as a small boy from Chateaugay, curious about what lay within, and more recently, as a man, he had come here to visit the chaplain: Father Booth.

But this was different. Now Father Booth was gone and it would be his own duty to unravel the mysteries hidden behind these tremendous gates. His excitement was different from what it had been when he had taken up his curacy at Ticonderoga—greater, even, than at his first appointment at Canton.

He had rung once and had half a mind to ring again. Guards let a huddle of trusties into the inner wire enclosure; his two bags grew heavy in the August sun.

Then he smiled.

He had never been kept waiting at Ticonderoga. Doors had swung open. A little too speedily perhaps? Maybe that is what the bishop had thought.

At last the guard was coming to the grille. The lock turned. A narrow portion of the great gate swung open.

"Well?" the guard asked.

"I'm Father Hyland."

"Yeah?"

"I'm the new chaplain."

"Uh-hu." The guard's eyes searched him, his glance lingering on the two black bags. "Wait a minute," he said.

He went back and muttered to another guard who was gathering the trusties together. The gate was ajar and through it now, in a gray line, began to trickle his new parishioners.

He could not look at them. It would be like staring at

cripples, peering too long at people who were disfigured, so he had only an impression of them as a moving grayness against the drab of the bastions.

They did not seem to be looking at him either, yet an inventory was being made of him—his height, his broad shoulders, the fine, high-bridged nose, the sensitive mouth that was on the verge of smiling, even the ears, set close to the skull. Only his eyes they did not meet.

Then he saw them go past the warden's feudal castle and up the street, and he realized that he had been inspected and had failed.

The guard came back then.

"O.K." He shut the priest within the gates and went over to a little stone house that was an excrescence on the wall. Telephoning, perhaps. The other guard, standing at the inner gate, gazed nowhere in particular. Beyond him stretched a long gray building, obviously a factory, and around it the hot waves of air were thickened by an odor of charcoal. Above ancient edifices, hewn of gray stone a hundred years before, the new red-brick buildings piled one upon another up a hill, itself browned and reddened by the August sun, and there, atop it, barns and silos determined not to be dwarfed by the tremendous turreted walls.

The walls were aimless. Through a discouraged, truncated triangle, splitting off about a third of the west side and dividing the red-brick building from a scarred open space, one wall ended abruptly; but stranger still was the purposeless length of ancient masonry that cut jaggedly and enormously into the middle of the eastern mountaintop.

The priest was jolted away from his observations by the bark of a voice from the guardhouse.

"What did you say your name was?"

"Hyland. Ambrose Hyland."

"Oh yeah?" The guard's voice had a note of incredulity. It made the new chaplain feel as he had when he was a small boy. He had hated the name and had made everybody call him "Steve." He smiled suddenly, thinking of himself as "Steve

Hyland, also known as Ambrose—height, 6 feet 2, prisoner No. 33,656, Clinton Prison, Dannemora, New York. Convicted——"

Convicted of being an ecclesiastical Robin Hood, for making converts in locker rooms and on the golf course, for having ideas about the liturgy, for having too many friends, for having rebuilt a church. Found guilty. Sentenced. A prisoner.

He felt like a convict when the guard said, "You can go in," and then, looking at the chaplain's black bags, "Won't need those."

"Where will I put them?"

"Over there."

He put the bags in the shade of the guardhouse and followed into an inner enclosure. The odor of the hemp factory was stronger.

"Where to?" he asked.

"How do I know?"

"I'm the new chaplain. I'm taking Father Booth's place."

"Is that so?"

"Yes, I am. Show me where to go," he said, surprised at his own gruffness.

The gate locked behind him. Somber hills with straggling dungeons and red-brick fortresses pressed down upon him. The heat flowed over everything, the smell.

The guard did not reply. Silently they went through gates, into a building, to a rotunda, up stairs. Men passed and did not look up. Men mopped floors and did not look up.

"Here's where you go," his escort said, and then left.

He was in what seemed to be a library. There were books, comfortable-looking chairs, a desk or two, and a canary. The bird had its head under its wing. Beneath the cage a sign hung: "Pete—Do Not Feed." He had no desire to feed canaries, but he went over and said, "Pete" two or three times. Then he felt foolish, and stopped.

For a moment he tried one of the chairs, stretched out his long legs, and rejected the idea of lighting a cigar. This could be all right, he told himself—not like Ticonderoga, but——

The quick smile came again. The poor bishop! He had been so sure that this assignment would be unwelcome.

"I'm sending you to be prison chaplain," the bishop had said.

"That's fine, Your Excellency."

"What do you mean?"

"I've had the best parish in the world. Now I'd like the worst."

"You'll get it, boy," the bishop had said. "You'll get your fill of it."

And here he was.

Well, he would have to be up and doing. If his parishioners did not come to him, he must go out to find them. And general facilities. He remembered that Father Booth had said Mass on the desk in the office, but there must be some other place, some chapel or something.

In the instant that he rose he knew what was wrong. This wasn't his office at all. It was the library. His quarters lay beyond, and he suspected what he would find. He went back to the canary's cage.

"Come on, Pete," he said. "We'll go through this together." With the uncaged bird on his shoulder he went in.

The office had been stripped. One desk, one raddled chair, leaning tipsily; brown stains on the walls, where pictures had hung; empty bookshelves, and, as a last indignity, the rug gone, and only the matting, tattered and brown, left behind. One more thing: a picture on the desk, with clear printing beneath it: "Padre Booth. A Man's Man. We Shall Not Look upon His Like Again."

With a chirp of disgust Pete leaped to the floor and began, with a kind of malevolence, to pull up the threads of the matting, like long worms, one by one. Even the bird seemed destructive, evil, like his new parishioners.

No.

He would not think of them like that. They were men. Convicts? Cons? Yes. But men.

He would be pro-con.

But where were they—*his* people?

2.   In Seattle, Washington, Brendon O'Malley was taking off on his first solo flight. To the left, splashed with noon, stretched Puget Sound; to the right, as if illuminated, lay Lake Washington. Between them the city climbed, washed and clean, from First Avenue to Capitol Hill. Below him toy traffic hastened to intersections and paused; little men hurried to street corners and, as if regulated by wires, stopped.

Brendon O'Malley loved the air, the city, the world. Above all he loved the freedom of flight.

In Greenwich Village, Carlos Santa Cruz daubed at the wall of Ruffino's. He was painting a palm tree and if it did not look very much like one he would say to Ruffino, "Tell 'em it's modern." If it were too bad he would say, "Tell 'em it's experimental."

He himself did not care about this phase of art. Here he let his flair for bright colors run riot, sprawled in large designs. It was a relief from the precision of his own work, which was almost too exacting, and while the currency which he reproduced was of large denominations, his success depended upon attention to minute details.

Carlos Santa Cruz was an engraver.

In Harlem, Lee Sapis Robinson was still asleep. It was better to sleep all day and to venture out only at night. He had been successful in avoiding the law for almost two weeks. As far back as he could remember, this was his longest period out of confinement.

If he were caught again, it would not be Sing Sing, but Dannemora and hell.

In Sokopolis, New York, the afternoon court was about to adjourn. For the hundredth time Allan Green said to the lawyer they had assigned to him, "I didn't do it!"

There was something fluky about the whole trial. He knew it. They were out to get him. The doctor's evidence had changed twice. It wasn't right. Today the doctor wasn't even here. They were out to get him.

He hadn't done it.

In all the post offices of the United States there were pictures, full-faced and profile, pictures uglier than passports.

"Wanted for Murder—Cyrus Turner—age thirty-two—five feet eleven—powerful build—gray eyes—noticeably large hands. This man is wanted for strangling."

In Sing Sing, Tom Riordan was writing another letter to Mr. Lehman.

Dear Sir! Since the act of clemency of the late governor, Alfred E. Smith, whereby I received a last-minute reprieve from the electric chair, I feel that my mental powers have been debilitated by durance vile. I consequently petition a transfer to Dannemora State Hospital for the Criminal Insane, as I am . . . as I have the opinion . . . as I am sure can be certified to . . . that I am not . . .

He crumpled the sheet of paper and threw it away, as he had done with all the others.

At Dannemora, in the Big Yard, Bud Horne and Dan Cassidy were together. They saw Dominic, good-natured, lying with his feet under a table, his head out, like a reversed ostrich. When the guard had gone by they both kicked Dominic, who got to his feet and followed them to the chaplain's office.

"Did you get the stuff to Bill?"

"Zex!"

"Butso! There's a roach."

Both exclamations meant for Dominic to be quiet, that a guard was near.

"Cop a mope," Bud Horne said. It meant to walk. They did.

Then Cassidy answered the first question. "Yep. He's in the icebox."

The icebox!

In solitary confinement Bill Martin saw them again.

There was nothing left to do. He had cached the cigarette that Big Dan Cassidy had smuggled to him; he had had moments of tattooing little hearts on his arm with a safety pin. There was nothing left except to see the scenes, just like a movie flashed on the walls.

He never saw his crime. That always had been hazy—twenty years ago. A trigger-happy soldier, he had shot a civilian buddy in a Plattsburg speak. What hit him was the trip here.

The snow was deep along the shoulders of the road. The car skidded and he caught his breath, hoping it would overturn. Roads went left through scrub oak and pine toward a ring of mountains. "Saranac Lake," one sign read. "Purina Chows," another sign read. He laughed, and they wondered why.

A whitewashed shack with all the eaves mustached with icicles blended into the snow beneath, and a barn and house across the road contrasted like poinsettias, the house white, trimmed with red, the barn red, trimmed with white snow, like Christmas.

Now there it was—a dark, red-brick mass surrounded by scratched fields sloping up steep hills. At the top there seemed to be a spire like a church. No, it was not. Closer up it was a barn and silo.

Past the State Hospital, under the walls—the terrible gray walls. The gates.

He saw them. They burned in the darkness. The gates of hell. . . .

3.   He would be pro-con.

The first ones he saw came almost half an hour after he had begun to wonder what his congregation would be like. He had consulted sparse index files, discovering that the population was 1,874 in the prison itself and 1,200 in the hospital. Perhaps he had been too filled up on gangster movies, but he was surprised at what he found. It was to take him almost three weeks to realize that there are no criminal types. He had tried to get in touch with the warden, but the switchboard operator said Warden Murphy was away. He had attempted to sit on the one chair in his office, but the broken spring tipped him forward abruptly. Then he heard a rustling from the library and he opened the door.

There were three men in the room.

Nearest the door, sitting at the good desk and rolling a white sheet of paper into a typewriter, was a young man in horn-rimmed glasses who looked like a bank clerk.

"Hello," Father Hyland said. "I'm your new boss, I guess."

The young man removed his spectacles, nodded slightly. He looked him up and down like a teller considering whether to cash a check and finally deciding it would be a bad risk.

"Who are you?" the priest asked.

"I'm Bud Horne." He put his spectacles on and typed.

The second man cleared his throat. As Father Hyland turned to him he saw a smile, suddenly frozen.

"You must have a name too," he said.

"No. Just a number."

"No name?"

"Not in here."

"I see." Father Hyland turned to the third man. "Have you?"

"Yeah. So's he. I'm Dan Cassidy. He's Dominic di Natale."

This man, the priest thought, graying about the temples, paunchy, might be a family man anywhere, the corner grocer, the foreman in a factory.

"Good. I'm glad to meet you."

The typewriter pounded unmistakably, "Now is the time . . . for all good men . . . to come to the aid . . . of the party . . ."

Father Hyland tried again. "You are working with me, aren't you?"

"We don't know yet," Cassidy answered.

"I see. Are there any more of you?"

"One."

"Is he coming in?"

"No."

"Why not?"

Dominic said, "They got him in the icebox."

"That's solitary," Cassidy explained.

"What for?"

Cassidy's glance was level. "He don't like fleas. That means informers that get something out of it. A job, for instance."

There was no more. The typewriter went on inexorably, "Now is the time . . . for all good men . . ."

The priest and Cassidy went back to Father Hyland's office. Pete, looking belligerent and forgotten, hopped about, a worm of thread in his bill.

Father Hyland spoke rapidly, without heat, "Look. I want the furniture you took out of there put back in."

"Do you?" Cassidy leveled at him.

"I expect it back by tomorrow morning. Now show me where the church is."

"The what?"

"The church. Come on. Get going."

In silence Cassidy and the priest went through the corridor, sternly washed down, smelling of disinfectant. They went into another building.

There was a moving-picture screen set up on a small stage, seats clamped to the floor, washings hung to dry. Band practice was drowned out by a clatter of dishes and of pots and pans banging from below, and by loud voices rising through thin flooring.

Pushed to one side on a stage, with a long kneeling bench leaning askew on it, was a makeshift altar surmounted by a small box, very shaky and also dirty. Whoever had thrown the kneeling bench had broken the altar stone.

"Is this it?" the priest asked.

"Yeah."

"This is the church?"

"Sure."

"I see."

"What's the matter with it?"

"Everything."

"It was good enough for Padre Booth."

"Was it?"

"Yeah."

"Well, get this—it isn't good enough for God."

CHAPTER TWO

The sun had disappeared over the Adirondacks but the evening was still bright with August. At their summer lodge to which he had hastened, Ambrose could see his mother bending over the open fire. Between them, with ripples barely visible, the narrows lay. He pushed the canoe a little harder, feeling the good impact of blade against solid water. It was cool now and he was at peace after the day.

"Hello!" he called. The echo came back from the perpendicular hillside across from the chalet.

His mother straightened up, refraining almost visibly from putting her hand on the small of her back. "Oh, it's you."

He shouted, "Sorry! Thought I'd get here sooner. You shouldn't have started that!"

Her voice was young, clear. "If I didn't, it'd never get done. Late as usual."

The canoe came smoothly over the reeds and whispered onto sand. He leaped out, almost at her feet, whirled her around, and took the toasting fork from her.

"Oh, you," she said.

"Oh, yourself. I've told you not to——" He had never managed to finish a sentence before she broke in.

"Had a bad day? First days are always bad."

"No more than I expected."

"Must have expected plenty. How many nice murderers did you meet?"

It came to him that she would be disappointed if he had not had a bad day. "It was hot. And the chapel wasn't very good."

"I suppose you'll want to fix it up." She seated herself in the garden chair. "Go slow, Ambrose. That's good advice, though what'd I know about it?"

"There's a lot to be done."

"No hurry. That's what broke you down at Ticonderoga, wasn't it?"

"I'm not sick. Everything's fine."

"Glad to hear it. When you do have anything on your mind you'd better write Mother Angela."

"Mother Angela?"

"Shame on you. She used to be Kitty Scanlon."

"Oh yes."

"She wrote me. They made her Mother Superior of the Carmelites in Philadelphia. These beans are good. Eat some. I bet you never answered her last letter."

He hadn't. There were plenty of letters unanswered. He preferred the telephone. He was glad now that he did not have to reply to his mother's question, because she was going on, "You didn't even write your own brother and sister you were coming. Mary and Gerald will be over tomorrow, though."

He had wondered about that—where his sister was tonight and why his brother's family wasn't here to celebrate his homecoming. It was only twelve miles to Chateaugay and it wouldn't have hurt them to come over.

"I wrote you, though," he said.

"Yes. I've got it laid down in lavender. I told them to come tomorrow. Didn't want them around tonight. We've always had such a crowd, Ambrose. Remember when there used to be fourteen at table? We never had dry eating like this, though. The beer's in the house in the ice chest."

He had forgotten, thinking as he rummaged through the icebox, that this was as close to sentimentality as his mother would ever come. She had wanted to be alone with him. Why hadn't he perceived that?

He heard her now, calling from outside, "The opener is in the living room on top of the McCormack records."

"I found it!"

"That's unusual. Bring out plenty. We'll take them out in the canoe."

He almost dropped the beer cans. "We're not going out——"

"Certainly are. I've got my old duds on. We don't waste a good night like this, canoe and all. Then, after we get back, you're going to play piano for me. And I promise not to sing."

2.   Mrs. O'Malley hurried to get down to the Maison Blanc on time. It was not so many blocks from the hospital, but her son Brendon would be impatient. She wished she had been able to get the hat from the Bon Marché, but the best she could do was to come in her nurse's uniform, her flat white heels tapping along the levels between hills. She would be late for Brendon. God bless him, he was a rascal!

She shouldn't have married an Irishman from the Klondike in the first place; in the beginning she had said that a combination of her name, of all names, Swedenberg, and O'Malley was all wrong. No wonder Brendon was a wild one.

She knew how he would feel after his first solo flight and she was relieved that he had not arrived. Yet seated on the black-walnut settle, she began to see, in her fancy, the women in boas and ostrich plumes and knee-length dresses, coming down the stairs. In some such place as this must once have been O'Malley had remembered her and died.

He had left her Brendon. That was enough.

Now he was here, and she did not want him to see her yet, so plain and white-clad, so obviously more accustomed to patients' complaints in aseptic hospitals than to such places as these. The young girls were looking at him, as of course they would—her Viking with Irish eyes.

"Mom!" he cried. "I made it!"

She was not surprised. "Of course you did."

"But I changed my mind. I don't want to waste my life."

Nor did O'Malley, she thought, late for the Klondike, late for the world war, trying to make up for it. Trying to live.

"Last time," she said, "it was the Lincoln Brigade. You were set on Spain. What is it now?"

"I saw Rainier. It was a big raspberry ice-cream cone. That's all it was. It isn't enough, Mom—not even the fight in Spain."

"What is enough, Brendon?"

"I want people to see the little world God made with His hands."

"Yes," she said. "That is enough." It was the part of his world O'Malley had surrendered when he married her. It was the strong Evangelicism she had given Brendon as part of his heritage.

"It is! I'm going to be a sky pilot. I'm going to study for the ministry."

She listened. Through the dinner she listened. It was wonderful. Yet somehow the ghost of O'Malley kept intruding through the enthusiasm of this incredible son of hers.

3.   The music had not soothed Father Hyland sufficiently, he feared. Through half the night he kept planning his sermon for Sunday. At Ticonderoga he had not worried this much. They had liked his talks there. They said they were cultured. Particularly the summer people. Sometimes they thought he was almost as good as his cousin, Monsignor Keegan, in New York. That was something. So why was he nervous about a gang of thieves?

The sheets wrinkled about him, and he could not, comfortably, get his long legs back into the bunk. Outside a whippoorwill was a needle stuck on a record. He would be glad when dawn came.

When it came, he was sound asleep. His mother woke him.

4.   Lee Sapis Robinson had to wait over until Monday. He felt better in jail because he was used to it, and though his cell mate was so drunk he couldn't talk much, this also was familiar. Things hadn't been much different, ever.

One thing bothered him. He had heard the Seventh Day Adventists singing "Beulah Land," and the verses kept repeating themselves over and over through the night. There was another land, and he didn't figure how he could ever reach it.

It wasn't there he was going now. It was to Dannemora.
He had asked, "What's the matter with Dannemora?"
"It stinks."
"I know that. How does it stink?"
"It just stinks, black boy, that's all. It just stinks."
There is a lovely land, far, far away . . .

5. As Father Hyland prepared for Mass that Sunday morning
there was a strange odor that assailed him. The fumes of breakfast were rising up from the mysterious regions below and they
were not appetizing. But there was something else, undefinable, the peculiar aroma of prison.

Someday he would have incense, clouds of it, to blot this out.
But now he had to be thankful that he had fresh linens from
the village convent and that his three secretaries had been efficient in propping up the altar and in helping him to vest. He
hoped that one of them would know how to serve Mass, but
when he turned to ask, there was no one there.

He had an acolyte, though, an old man with dried hair
matching the gray of his uniform, seeming somehow brittle,
as he bent low, answering the responses in perfect if some-
what Germanic Latin.

Then came the moment to speak for the first time to his
flock, his black sheep. He turned, and as he looked at his congregation, again he was amazed. Out of all who should have
been there, there were perhaps a hundred scattered about, with
one strangely ostracized group midway back, cut off from the
rest. But those who were there might have constituted a congregation at a men's mission anywhere. There were young
boys, blond and blue-eyed; there were old men, substantial,
prosperous, he would have said; there were the middle-aged
with hard cheekbones but not hard eyes. This was, he would
have thought, a middle-class congregation, like the six-thirty
on Sunday. He looked in vain for lantern jaws and bulged
crania.

"Men," he began, "I'm not going to keep you long this
morning. I have only one thing to say to each of you. Both

of us have been sent here and both of us must make our lives here. The bishop sent me and the state sent you and together we must work out our salvation.

"You have not yet had your real trial and judgment. That comes after life is over, when God is your judge. He, not man, gives the final sentence—to heaven, or hell.

"Now you and I have to help each other to get ready for that sentence. That's what we are here for. Together we can do it. I promise to pray for you, but I can't say your prayers for you. I'll say Mass and administer the Sacraments; I can't hear Mass or receive the Sacraments for you. That is up to you.

"And you can pray for—and with me."

He was stumbling now, and he knew it. He finished abruptly—"because God knows, I need it."

He blessed himself. This had not been the sermon he had intended to preach at all.

6. The hearts which Bill Martin had tattooed on himself had festered and hardened and he had picked the scabs off in the dark. He began to ache for a cigarette. If he had been allowed out for Mass he could have cadged one.

He had a right to go to Mass. He would send for the new chaplain and make him fight for him—find out if he was a right guy like Father Booth.

Why was he here? Because he socked a roach for making a dirty remark about Booth. That's why. He was a martyr.

He felt better about being a martyr, but then, as usual, when he was hungry and it was dark, he began to see flamingoes, big, white-pink flamingoes——

Got to stop this. That's the way guys went over the other side—to the State Hospital—stir-crazy.

Thomas Riordan, Sing Sing, Ossining, New York: Excellency: Am petitioning that an examination be made of me in re sanity, and transference to Dannemora State Hospital for Criminal Insane. Advise immediate action, as have homicidal tendencies.

That was all he wrote. He signed it quickly and sent it. It was read by the principal keeper and was held in his office. But an investigation was begun.

7. Around him, that morning after Mass, and even during his thanksgiving, Father Hyland could feel an inexplicable aura of evil. He tried to analyze it. It was not caused by the desertion of his secretaries. In a way he had expected that. Certainly it was not due to the congregation. He could not understand it. A wave of opposition? But he had met with that yesterday and he had not felt like this.

All through his prayers he was bothered, and it was more than a distraction. He was glad when he could rise and prepare to go outside the gates for his second Mass at the State Hospital.

Everyone had left the auditorium. There were sounds from remote depths of dishes being stacked, but otherwise he was alone. Loneliness on lakes and mountains he had understood since boyhood, but this aloneness in the midst of multitudes was a new thing. This also he must conquer. But there was more—something else.

As he went back to his office he tried to brush off the sensation but it would not go. Except for the lay figures of the guards at their posts there was no one. Behind each barred window was a man. In back of each tommy gun in the turrets was a watcher. The sense of a thousand eyes on him in the solitude might explain it. But inside here there was no one. So he came out onto the balcony where he could look down on the approaches to West Hall.

Then from the doorway a small knot of prisoners came, carrying band instruments. On his balcony he was high enough above the rotunda so that the men looked unreal, marching in uncertain formation, automatic, unhuman.

Silently, without flurry, a group knotted together. Silently, mechanically, they resumed walking. Except one. A gray figure, clutching his belly, crawled up the stairs toward the infirmary.

The gray line halted. Out of the silence came a blare of sirens and the priest ran down the hall, down the stairs. Guards were about him. In the rotunda the line of prisoners stood, immobile. Only guards and priest hurried. Only around them was sound. The convicts were silent.

Etched with the precision of nightmare, he saw the guards, drawn guns, artillery trained from the turrets, the static figure on the infirmary landing over which he knelt.

"I'm the priest," he was calling.

A guard, frantic, bending beside him, calling, "Who done it?" And his own voice saying, "Go away. Leave us alone." And louder, "I'm the priest!"

Then he heard the dying man. "Father Booth, thank God." The man did not open his eyes. He did not look at him. The other prisoners, the sun bright on the brasses, were led away.

He listened closely for the whisper. "Two years. We fought. Tell him—if he comes to see you—I done wrong to fight for it—just a band instrument——"

"Just what?"

"A tuba. It was his. I shouldn't have fought him for it."

"You mean that's why he killed you? Just for that?"

"Sure. That's enough—in here."

Someone interfering again—a white-smocked doctor.

"Go away," the priest said. "This is my job."

"Hey, are you listening?"

"Yes."

"He'll come to you—tell him my fault——"

"Sure. He didn't mean to——"

"He meant to. Yeah. Say, are you the Padre?"

"Yes. I'm the Padre."

The doctor again, attendants, a futile stretcher. Light, far off, on the band instruments, where the convicts, under heavy guard, were being led away.

"O.K. Swell guy—Padre Booth—guts. You got guts."

Then the guard again, "Who done this to you?"

And the priest shouted at him to go away.

"Padre Booth?"

"Yes."

"I'm no fink. I won't even tell you who done it. Now shoot the works."

"You're sorry for all you have done?"

"God! God——"

While his hand was raised in absolution there was a convulsion and for a moment the man was real, a human being, dying.

Afterward there were voices saying, "They're calling from the State Hospital. Is there going to be Mass?"

"Yes," the priest said. "Yes."

8. The judge, at Sakopolis, was at breakfast. He was angry with his wife because, like a woman, she was taking that Green's side.

"Sure," he said, "we got him on a technicality. That's what my job is. I give those fellows the book."

"I feel sorry for his wife."

"How about his victim? Ever think of her? You got to think about society too. I'd rather have straight murder than cases like this."

"The papers were hard on you, dear."

"That's politics."

"But Green didn't plead guilty, did he?"

"Of course not. They never do. He was just an ugly drunk—beat the girl up. Even the doctor wasn't a good witness. But we got grounds for conviction. That's what matters."

"I know. But what did Green plead?"

"Innocent. What they all do." He dipped again into the puffed rice. "What they all do—innocent."

9. At the State Hospital Father Ambrose Hyland turned around for the sermon. He would give them the same thing he had given at prison. He saw them and he couldn't—the vacant faces, the several under durance, the different, the anxious, and the blank—the lost. But it seemed to him then, as he looked at them, that at least this small section of his

flock had received some great grace. It was not a fleeting impression, but was to remain with him for years. So he saw them—whatever crimes they had committed, now washed out, cleansed, burned pure.

At last, innocent.

CHAPTER THREE

The next day Ambrose Hyland was determined to carry on as though nothing had happened. He had managed well at Chateaugay during the Sunday dinner with his sister Mary, his brother Gerald, and their families. He had chatted about old times and had even played and sung for them as he had done when they had all lived together. Yet under the warm feeling of homecoming lay the vision, the unreality. A gray line. A pause. Marching on. Screaming sirens and death. The casual murder over a band instrument caught him between syllables and choked him.

This morning, he resolved, would be different. A year ago he had joked with his university friends when they said he would be shocked at something. "I haven't been shocked since I was six years old," he had said, but he had meant something much more medieval and much more monastic, that it was the duty of the priest never to be shocked. He must understand, sympathize, excoriate, absolve. But the ills of original sin must never surprise him.

He would go on as though nothing had happened.

But this was too much. It would have been easy had he alone been calm in the midst of excitement; but this was all wrong. There should not be the routine, unbroken, undisturbed morning. The trivial reason for murder was unnerving; the matter-of-fact acceptance of crime was itself criminal.

There were three tabs on his desk. A tab, he had discovered, was a note from the men. He tried to rise, to call for an explanation, but the broken spring in his chair tipped him forward. The annoyance was a relief onto which he could turn his anger.

He called for Horne to come in. "What are these things?"

"It's the way we do things here. That's a requisition."

The requisition exactly duplicated the furniture in the outer office, ending sardonically, "One yellow canary—cage to match."

"These aren't what I asked for," Father Hyland said.

"If you want 'em—that's the way to get 'em."

"I see. If I want them. I don't think I want them—that much."

Tomorrow he could bring over a chair and a typewriter. A rug would be a nuisance. He would remove the matting himself.

"That's your business," Horne said.

"Yes. It is. What's this next thing?" He looked at a formal paper made out in Cassidy's handwriting.

"It's a requisition for a church."

"Why?"

"Cassidy says you don't like what we got."

The priest tore the sheet across and threw the pieces in the wastebasket. He unlocked the desk drawer and took out a box of cigars, slitting it open with his penknife.

"Have one?"

"No."

"All right. What's this?"

"It's a tab from Bergner."

"What does that mean?"

"He wants an interview."

"What do I do about it?"

"Call the guardhouse."

"That's all?"

"Yes. He's in an idle company."

"Does that mean something?"

"It means he don't work."

"You mean he won't work?"

"Nope."

"Doesn't everybody have to work—hard labor?"

"Not at Dannemora."

"Why?"

"I don't know. Just you don't have to work if you don't want to."

"I asked you why."

"I told you. That's just the way it is."

"Don't you ever ask questions?"

"Nope."

"Not even—when there's—a murder?"

"That's when we don't." Bud Horne smiled.

"I see," the priest said. "Maybe I'd better not either. Is that it?"

"That's it."

"Thanks. I get it. Is there any other—business?"

"Yes."

"What is it?"

"The warden wants you should call soon as you get in."

"Why didn't you let me know?"

"How can you tell when a chaplain's going to be in?"

"What do you mean by that?"

"You weren't here last Sunday, were you?"

"No. I wasn't supposed to be."

"We were ready for you. It was lucky you didn't come."

The priest puffed for a moment on his cigar. "Ring the warden," he said.

"O.K."

The warden's voice sounded reassuring on the phone. "That you, Father? I'm sorry I was away over the week end. I hear the boys gave you a hard time yesterday. Would have been worse a week ago, but we stopped that."

"I just heard something. What was going to happen?"

"Oh—they were ready to gang up on you. No worries now, though."

"I'll get used to it," the priest said. "And to murder——"

He heard a chuckle. "Oh—that doesn't happen every day. But say—you going to be in for a while?"

"Certainly."

"Good. I'll run over in half an hour."

"Fine, but I'll come to see you."

"No, you won't. I'll be there." The connection was broken off.

Which should he do first, the chaplain wondered—go to the infirmary or visit his secretary in solitary confinement? Perhaps he should attend to the living first. He could arrange for the funeral later.

It was a beautiful day. He strolled up a brick pathway trying to memorize a position of the buildings. He knew where the infirmary was and he never would forget the rotunda. The scarred hillside, he had learned, was the Big Yard. The little yards—courts, you called them—were between buildings. He did not mind looking into them where the men took the air, but sometime today he must begin his tour of the cells. He did not like the idea. It would be hard to talk to men in cages.

A guard told him how to find segregation. It was a weird entrance he made, reminding him of those tortuous passages at Coney Island—the long hall, dimly lighted with uncanny green lights, running underground, a locked elevator, a higher but still subterranean passage, and at last the gallery.

"Martin's cell, four down," the guard said. When he reached the place, suddenly, blindingly, an electric light went on. He saw a creature, emaciated, stripped to the waist, pricked and scabbed with self-inflicted cicatrices.

"What do you want?" the prisoner asked.

"Bill Martin. He's my secretary."

"I'm him."

"Can I do anything for you?"

"You bet. You know what."

"No, I don't."

"Didn't you get my tab?"

"No. I just wanted to see you."

"That schlepp!"

"What?"

"The roach—the guard, to you. He told me he'd get it out to you. Say! What'd you come for?"

"I just wanted to see you."

"Take a good look."

For the first time the inmate raised his head. Father Hyland was surprised at what he saw—a face of great beauty, though with an El Greco distortion, an elongation of forehead, a pear-shaped bone structure rarely seen except in medieval tapestries. It should have been peering out of a fringe of unicorns and battlements; it fitted too perfectly into this bizarre background of dungeon, green darkness, and sudden light. Only the voice, the accent, was wrong.

"They wouldn't let me out to church yesterday. They got no right to keep me away."

The priest did not know what rights prisoners had. He employed a technique he had often found successful when he had been a curate.

"Tell me about it."

"What gives? You're supposed to know the answers."

"I'm new here. I'll fight for you, but I don't know what I can do yet."

The strange, dark eyes peered at him. "You can get me out of this hole, can't you? You know why I'm in."

"No. I don't. Nobody told me."

"Can't you find out?"

"There are a lot of things around here I can't seem to find out."

Bill Martin laughed sardonically. "So the boys won't talk."

"Will you?"

"Some things. What do you want to know?"

"Mainly about Father Booth. What happened?"

"As if you didn't know."

"I don't."

"That ain't the way we heard it."

"I don't understand all this. There was a picture in my office——"

"I put it there."

"Why?"

"Because it's true. You're bigger than Padre Booth. But you'll never be the man he was."

"That may be. He is a great man."

"You can say that again."

"He's a good friend of mine."

For a moment Bill Martin looked up with an expression of surprise and of self-doubt. Then he said slowly, "They got him. They put guards following him. Every place he went."

"Why?"

"You'll find out."

The insinuation was incredible, the priest thought. Probably some quirk of a prison mind. He would ignore it.

"Look, Bill, tell me what I can do for you."

"Now?"

"Yes."

"Right now?"

"Certainly."

"Right now you can get out of here."

"But I mean——"

"Scram!"

Then he would say no more. He turned his head away, and no matter what the priest said to him, the reply was only silence. There was nothing for it but to leave.

On the way back to the office he kept wondering. Why did the prisoners suspect him? Out of a clear sky the bishop had sent him here. The last time he had seen Father Booth was at the diocesan retreat, where, though he had been genial as always, he had not looked like a well man. It was true—he had looked haunted.

Back at the office he was glad that the warden had not yet arrived and that the old man who had served Mass was waiting.

"I am Max Bergner, my Father."

There was an Old-World quality about his courtesy.

"I'm glad to see you," the priest said. "Sit down. Have a cigar."

He reached for the fresh box that he had opened that morning. There were no cigars left. And he remembered that there was only one chair. It was a relief to remember that Bergner preferred to stand and did not smoke.

"Thanks for serving my Mass," Father Hyland began, making conversation.

"I would like to serve your Mass always."

"Of course." He remembered the idle companies and thought he would make a point. "I hear you don't work. At least serving Mass will give you something to occupy your time."

"Yes, my Father. But I do not find my time unoccupied."

"No? I should think you would."

"Father Booth gave me books. I would like more."

"Glad to get you some. That's another part of my job, they tell me. How about *The Bridge of San Luis Rey*—or maybe that's a little deep."

"I would read it."

"What have you been reading?"

"Rodriguez on Christian Perfection. Then, the *Autobiography of the Little Flower*. Then I read *St. John of the Cross* and *St. Teresa of Avila*. Now, Your Reverence, I would like *De Caussade*."

Father Hyland wished he had a cigar. All he could do was whistle. This man had gone through ascetical theology and was working in advanced mysticism. The priest was glad that there was an interruption. Dominic came in beaming, announcing that Warden Murphy was there.

Bergner said, "Excuse me. I will wait," and had gone before he could be stopped. There was a certain relief in seeing him go.

Warden Murphy was as genial as his voice had promised. He looked around the bare office.

"Guess the boys got busy in here. They always do. We'll send you more stuff tomorrow."

"Thanks. There were no books—precious little in the files, even. I was going to bring over some furniture, but what happened yesterday drove it out of my mind."

"It would. Don't get the idea that's routine stuff around here."

"I'm glad you said that. Everybody just kept going about their business."

"Yes. I know. They always do."

"It's—sort of horrible."

"It must seem so. It isn't quite that bad."

"How do you explain it?"

"Fright. The men are scared. Discipline is always better for a few days after a thing like that. You see, they're all saying that they don't know a thing about it. Just minding their own business."

"You mean it does affect them? They don't show it."

"They don't dare. They know we have the whole band outfit in confinement. We're putting the screws on them to find out who did it and why."

It came to Father Hyland, with grim humor, that in a single day, as a priest, he knew more about one inside matter in the prison than the warden.

"You'll find the reason, I suppose?" he asked.

"Probably not. But we'll try. We're not very progressive around here, but we get along."

"But so many men saw it! Someone will talk."

"Can't be sure. They hate what they call a 'fink'—and they're afraid of what would happen to them if they did squawk."

"What could?"

"Oh, sometimes they play football. Accidents happen. You know."

"Just like that?" He sighed. "I suppose I'll get used to it."

"Don't. As soon as you do, you're washed up here. Never get used to anything. But this isn't what I came over to say. Where do you plan to live?"

"I don't know. I've been staying at my mother's cottage."

"That's too far away. Why don't you come to our place?"

"That's awfully nice of you but——"

"We've got plenty of room. The Mrs. and I call it the Ark."

"Perhaps for a few days until I find a place."

"Good. That's settled. Move in on us any time you want. Stay as long as you want."

Father Hyland had wished, all through the meeting, that the prisoners had left him some cigars. He was unused to being remiss in hospitality. All his life he had been giving, doing things for others. This experience was acutely embarrassing.

"I wish I could thank you," he said.

"Don't try. I'll be in your debt soon enough. We all will, here."

After the warden had left, he prayed that he might someday be of service again. It was hard, now, to see how it could come about. Well, he thought, going hurriedly out of the office, at least he could bury the dead.

"I'm going over to the infirmary," he said to Bud Horne. Then he stopped and smiled. Riding up and down on the carriage of the inexorable typewriter was Pete, the canary.

The typewriting stopped. Pete lifted one delicate foot with curved pink claws, replaced it deliberately, and flew with a chirping to the priest's shoulder.

Bud Horne pushed back the typing table abruptly.

"You can't have him," he said.

"I seem to have him already," the priest replied.

"He's mine."

Father Hyland held up his fingers and Pete leaped to it. "Here," he said, "I know he's yours. Take him."

Bud Horne reached out his finger toward Pete. "Come on, fellow," he said. "Come here where you belong."

Pete was reluctant. He cocked his head and gazed at the priest.

"Pete!"

It was the voice of the master, and Pete obeyed.

Father Hyland left the office. One old gray figure, unobtrusive, unnoticed, continued to read and to wait.

On the way to the infirmary Father Hyland kept thinking, "Three things today. Bergner will read books. Warden Murphy is kind. A bird flew to me."

He met a white-coated attendant at the morgue door.

"I've come to arrange about the Mass," he said.

"What Mass?"

"The Mass I'm going to say for the poor fellow who—got killed yesterday."

"He don't get no Mass."

"I'm the one to decide that."

"Where are you going to give it to him? Do you think we want a stiff in the mess hall?"

"What do you do?"

"Keep 'em awhile. Then if the family don't claim 'em we get rid of 'em."

"How?"

"Wrap 'em up in a sheet."

"I see. That's all?"

"Yup."

"What did Father Booth do for them?"

"What could he do? Oh, he went down to the grave with them. That's at the bottom of the hill—over the tracks, in the swamp."

"Didn't he say Mass for them?"

"Maybe. I don't know. But anyhow he didn't have the body around when he did."

"Not even Mass?"

"Listen—get this. You're lucky to have Mass at all. When Chaplain Booth first came here he couldn't have Mass more than two Sundays a month. Get that? He fought for it. We have it regular now. That's all you have to have, isn't it?"

"No."

"What else do you need?"

"Some place to bury the dead."

"No can do."

"There must be some way."

"There ain't."

"If you had a chapel——"

"Yeah. *If!*"

"Then we'll—we'll have to have one."

"Sure. That's a good idea. Sure."

The attendant was smiling, and the smile was not good to look at.

He went back to the office. He felt physically ill. No place for a decent funeral. Even the dead, here——

Max Bergner was waiting.

Then in the barren office the priest heard the story of a man who told him that he had been a murderer once, long ago, and went on to a revelation of years of contrition, of a monastic life, and a spirituality as profound as the priest had ever heard even in his direction of cloistered nuns.

When Max Bergner was gone, Father Hyland put his head down on the desk. He was shaken. Suddenly he saw himself. He had kept this man waiting while he chatted with the warden. He had forgotten about him after he had hurried over to the infirmary.

He had talked to the warden. He had felt good, secure, privileged. A canary had preferred him to Bud Horne. He had liked that. What was the matter with him? Why had the bishop sent him here? He would never be another Father Booth, who had fought even to have Mass. He must see Father Booth.

It was a wrenching moment. He had, he discovered, expected to find crime among criminals.

It was terrifying to find sanctity.

CHAPTER FOUR

In his hideout in the Adirondacks Cyrus Turner looked down at his huge hands. He had seen the signs in the post office, and he knew now what it was like to be hunted. It was a coldness at the indrawing of breath. It was a thought behind consciousness.

He had known that when he was composing he could escape from himself. Now there was no piano. He could not compose. There was no escape.

He had never sold very much. All his friends knew of him as a composer, an artist, and they had been glad to keep him for week ends, for summers even, when he found the right words to say at large dinners. There had been charming hostesses who had placed him beside their daughters and had noted that he had the correct taste in wines.

It had been a feeble existence. The thing that struck him most now was the vacuity, even the bitterness of the humor— what they had laughed so much about. He had tried, during his weeks of escape, to read the books of humor. They were all sour. There was nothing that was healthy. He hummed over his own themes. They also were diseased. There was a wet rot in the chord progressions. No wonder he had done what he had done.

Suddenly he had stood up. Hazardville, Connecticut, improbable, inconceivable name for such a place. The cabin, wood-fire smoked, extremely artistic, had shaken before to violence, but there had been no depth to the arguments—nothing until Ralph spoke sneeringly of Mona.

Cy Turner loved her. That was all. She was everything they could say about her. It was all true. But Ralph had no right to say it. He had done it for her. He had—the detective-story phrase kept pummeling him—"shot his belly full of lead."

Then were the misty moments, the last discordant, decadent collapse of Ralph's hands on the keys. Then the escape from nothing. No need had been to take the road. But the swamp, the rotten-swamp smell, dragging his sucking feet out of ooze —through a chicken farm, through the good scorching of brambles to a railroad, until, pretending to be drunk, he had got somehow to Springfield, Albany, here.

There was no cause for lament. Only that after he had shot Ralph—he had always been very fond of him—and he had seen that it was not fatal—Ralph had been a good friend of his—he should not have—Ralph shouldn't have told him he was wrong about Mona—he shouldn't have put his hands around Ralph's throat—trying to lift him up—tightening——

He looked at his hands. "God," he said, "I'll do something

else with them. I'll never play again. I'll work with them somehow."

At the last he had felt, beneath his power, such a slight
yielding, heard such a slight gasp, a gurgle.

He hadn't done it. How could any reasonable man do that
to his best friend?

2. He had not found Father Booth, after all, but he had found
something else. On his way out the gate he encountered a knot
of men, entering. "On a draft," they called it.

"Hello!" You could not welcome men here. "I'm the chaplain. Come and see me any time you want."

A very black boy grinned at him. "I'm Lee Sapis Robinson.
Do you know Father Ayde in Baltimore? Ever been down to
Sing Sing?"

"I'm sorry, no," the priest said. "But you've certainly been
around."

"Most every place. I likes variety." He laughed.

Another man broke in. "My name's Riordan. I'll be with—
the mentally unwell. I've done a little library work. I'd like to
help."

Then the guard at the inner gate signaled the inmates. Most
of them smiled at the priest, and one of the sullen ones looked
up as he passed. The corn yellow of his hair was in striking
contrast to the brown of his eyes. And such eyes! An expression such as one sees only in a wounded animal.

Father Hyland put his hand on the boy's shoulder. "What's
your name, son?"

The lad kept walking. "I can't talk, I guess."

"I'll look you up."

They were at the gate, and the priest prayed that some
noise would drown out the sound of its closing. The gate
clanged shut.

The boy called back, "I'm Allan Green," and was lost among
the others.

It would be possible, the priest thought, to let Father Booth
have his older congregation and to build up a new loyalty

among the incomers. There was hope there. And there was greater hope when he found a guard with one foot on the running board of his car.

"I just got off duty," the guard said. "I thought I'd wait and meet you. I'm Joe Hogan. I work here."

"Glad to see you. Can I give you a lift?"

"Any place you're going. I'd like a chance to talk to you."

"I'm going up to see Father Booth."

"Swell. Can I come? I'd give a lot to see him."

Together they went the many miles through the mountains to the town where the former chaplain had his parish, and though Joe Hogan was discreet, Father Hyland had many of the rumors which he had heard confirmed. He learned of an uphill fight from a time, fifteen years ago, when the dead had been thrown into quicklime. He began to understand what the constant battles of his predecessor had achieved. Surely there was still much to accomplish. Tremendous things. But Father Booth had started with nothing.

When they arrived at the little country rectory, they were met by the housekeeper. No. Father Booth was not at home. He wouldn't be at home. She had taken one look at the uniformed guard, and that was that. There wasn't any use to wait. Hadn't the poor Father suffered enough with the guards after him? She bit her tongue when that slipped out.

So that also was true. Perhaps everything was true. Now Father Hyland, piecing things together, began to get a picture of what had happened, of a man fighting for the prisoners and for the rights of God, through the years building unavoidable antagonisms, until at last authorities thought of him as dangerous and defiant. And the loyalty of the inmates? Why not? To the man who had sacrificed everything for them.

The housekeeper softened as they were leaving. "Don't try to see him yet, Father," she said. "It would hurt too much. His heart is still there. He still had plans. He had so much left to do at Dannemora."

"But he can't blame me for any of this, can he?" Father Hyland asked.

She was shocked. "Blame you? Glory be to God, you're his only hope. You'll do what he wanted to do."

What he wanted to do? Kneeling for a visit in the dark little church—the door had swung crazily on broken hinges—Father Hyland made his resolve. It was, when it came, quite simple, and without emotion. The other day his statement that they must build a church had seemed reasonable enough. But now it was imperative.

He did not know whether the building of a church had been part of Father Booth's plan, or whether his dreams had dared go so far. But at least it was a logical carrying on of what had already been achieved. Perhaps he would be asked to follow in the same pattern, to fight all the way, even to personal defeat. Very well. He was ready. If Christ, leaning from the cross above him, had taught His priests any lesson at all, it was the lesson of individual defeat. The Crucifixion. But beyond that——

Then, suddenly, he knew. There was more than that. Beyond Golgotha was redemption and resurrection. Even in the midst of immolation there was a voice saying, "This day thou shalt be with me in Paradise." And it was said to a thief by a condemned man on a cross. So he knew.

"Saint Dismas," he prayed, "the Good Thief on the Cross, help me to build a church. For men like you. And for men like us. Father Booth and myself. Somehow, Saint Dismas, help us to build a church."

He rose then and went out to where Joe Hogan was waiting.

"Sorry you didn't get to see Padre Booth," Hogan said as they began the drive back.

"But I did. I saw him better than I ever saw him. And a lot of other things too. Only one thing bothers me now. I can't believe the warden was against Father Booth."

"He wasn't. They'll blame him, of course—like they do other people. But he had as much to do with it as you have."

"I see," he said. "I'm glad."

"There were some—— Why talk about it? Look. Warden Murphy's in back of you. So am I."

"Thanks. No matter what I do?"
"No matter what."

3. The new men were disbursed. Lee Sapis Robinson was singing a hymn tune down at the end of the cell block. Tom Riordan, assured that he would be in the State Hospital within a few days, was already planning how, with the prison chaplain's help, he could build a library, build an interest in men like him who were dim with years of confinement; how he could spend his life doing greater good than ever he had done outside.

Greeney sat in his cell, his head down. The latrine, the bed, the table, this chair. And the bars.

"God, you can't do this," he was saying. "You gotta be fair. You gotta get me out of here. I don't know how You're going to do it, but You have to find a way. See? Because I done a lot of dirty, rotten things in my life, but I never done what they put me here for. See?"

Greeney's head was down and nobody could see how he looked.

The next day at noon silence was called in the mess hall. The clatter of knives and forks stopped. The new chaplain wanted to speak. Most of the men looked up at him. He seemed very dark, very tall. It was as if something new had come to him.

"Men," he said, "yesterday I went over to see my old friend, Father Booth. I didn't see him, as it turned out, but I saw a lot of other things. He had plans for you. I don't know how far they went. But he believed in them. And he believed in you. And so do I.

"He never stopped. He didn't think things were finished. And now, they tell me, they are finished. I don't believe that.

"They tell me what we want can't be done. They tell me you won't help me. I don't believe any of that. But I have one belief. This is it:

"Men, so help me God, we're going to build a church."

CHAPTER FIVE

"So you're going to build a church."

The warden was not looking at Ambrose Hyland but at the back of the silent trusty who was waiting with the Sunday breakfast coffee.

"Yes, sir, I am. I told the men."

"So I heard. You know what you're up against, don't you?"

"I think so."

"I wonder."

The warden paused while the trusty served him his toast. He broke off a piece and pointed with it at the priest.

"Look here," he said. "Suppose I promise you your church. Soon as I finish the new cell blocks. How will that be?"

"How soon can I have it?"

"Next thing. We need the cell blocks too. You know that."

The trusty was listening. You could see that, in his stiffened back. Three of the buildings, made of old, gray, native stone, were a hundred years old and the conditions in them were deplorable.

"And *you* need a church too," the priest said.

"Yes. I admit it. I've seen the need. So I'll get a church."

"Thanks. I thought you were against it."

"I'm not against a church. I'm only against that scheme of yours for a separate Catholic chapel."

"I never proposed that."

"Oh?"

"I want three separate chapels."

"Ridiculous."

"Why?"

"Can't you get along with Rabbi Schoenkopf and Mr. Bay well enough to arrange your service in the same place?"

"I'm speaking for them too. We all want it. It's just that we do get along so well that makes us want separate places of worship."

"Can't be done. I'll give you a nice chapel under the new mess hall."

"So that the breakfast noises will be on top of us instead of under us. And look—you're a Catholic. You know what I'm talking about. Where am I going to reserve the Blessed Sacrament? What is Mr. Bay going to do—shove his cross out every time the rabbi comes in? That may be all right in army camps, where you can't do any better. But there's no need for it here. Dannemora isn't like that. We're permanent."

Warden Murphy laughed. "You bet we are—I hope. But you still can't do it. There's never been a denominational chapel on government property. Can't be done."

"Then we'll be the first to do it."

"Hold on. I said we can't. There won't be any appropriation for that sort of thing."

"I know. So each of us chaplains will raise our own money."

"That isn't all. You'd have to get land to build on. Government land. Then your church would belong to the state. Would your bishop allow it? And what about the work? Tools brought in—escape hazards——"

"There won't be trouble. The men will work."

"What?"

"You've got seven hundred men in idle companies. Is that good?"

"No. It's rotten."

"You could sell the commissioner on that. It would put the men to work."

"Maybe the unions would object."

"Why? There'd be no interference with free enterprise if men were building their own church in here, would there?"

"No." The warden stirred his coffee. "Say," he added with surprise, "you're pretty practical."

"Didn't you think I was?"

"No—to be honest with you. I never thought of priests that way."

Father Hyland smiled. He remembered the job he had just

finished of rebuilding the church in Ticonderoga, of the endless details he had left behind. He thought of the thousands of pastors who had built churches, schools, hospitals——

"We're not just dreamers. We're builders too."

"And fighters." Warden Murphy laughed. "I shouldn't have forgotten that. Maybe you'll win." .

"I haven't any doubt about it."

"I have. But perhaps it'll be worth the fight. Look, now." He brushed some crumbs into a small heap. "You come around tomorrow and we'll go over all the details. I'll tell you the problems you'll have to meet with the state officials."

"I'll add some—the problems with religious officials. I'm not fooling myself. It's not going to be easy."

"Maybe harder than you think."

"Maybe."

"It's going to be a strain on you. I wish you'd reconsider about living here for a while. At least the Mrs. and I could look after you—see you get fed and get some rest. How about coming back for a few weeks? At least until I can get you some place to live."

Both men had stood up. The trusty was listening.

"No, sir, thanks. I appreciate it. But I can't stay here."

"Why not?"

"I'm the prisoners' chaplain. I'm their man."

"I see."

"I can't play it both ways. I hope I'll never have to be against you, but I will have to be for them."

"You're right."

"You see, sir, I'm—pro-con."

As they shook hands, the warden whispered, as much as his booming voice would let him, "Don't tell anybody, Father—but so am I."

So the chaplain went down the stairs that morning with new buoyancy in his stride which had not been there since he had come to this place, and it was not due only to the gruff kindliness of the warden. Something else had happened. For the first time.

The listening trusty had offered to carry his two bags to the door.

2. The rains had come to Seattle. Grayness in the west choked the Cascades and to the southeast shrouded Mt. Rainier. Brendon O'Malley felt shut in.

He put on his raincoat and walked down to the market, where there were always people, and where fresh vegetables piled on stalls were a brightness. Then on his way back to Pine Street he stopped in at the Catholic Seamen's Club.

He had no right here, a Protestant divinity student, but they let him play checkers with the old salts and even join in the endless religious arguments that were always in full swing. At first these arguments had spoiled his pleasure in the place, but, later, they began to give him a zest for his studies, a practical meaning to them, as if a world were opening.

From his books came a new pleasure. He could forget the grayness about him in his realization of the expanses of the mind. He had found a liberty of living and thinking which had nothing to do with the circumstances of exterior forces. He felt free as he had never felt in the limitlessness of the air.

Nothing, he thought, could ever close him in again.

3. In his cell, Greeney paced up and down, paced up and down—walking and walking, from end to end, paced up and down——

It had been all right when he was speaking with the chaplain. Once—twice—it had been all right. Then there was nothing—nothing else.

Greeney paced up and down, paced up and down, walking and walking——

Nothing he could do. Nothing to do. Nothing they would let him do.

In the next cell he could hear a man pacing up and down. If you kept step with him you would go crazy; if you didn't, you would go crazy.

Why didn't the priest do something? The priest knew he

was innocent. Didn't he? He was the only man here who was innocent.

Paced up and down. Paced up and down. Paced up and down.

4. Bill Martin saw no particular reason to be grateful. Father Hyland had got him out of solitary, but that was small credit to him after all this time. Still, it was good to be back in the office and to feel once more the crisp October air. Yet even the wind inside the walls was different. The breeze was fresh only on top of the hill where the silo stood. Maybe that was why the chaplain walked up there so often, doing funny things, seeming to measure off spaces with his quick, long strides.

Every once in a while Bill Martin had got himself put in solitary, just for the experience, then just for the change, because it was different when you got out again. After solitary, the regular life was an improvement; for a while it did not seem so bad. The only way you could get a lift in this place was to get into a worse jam, and then when you got out of it, you would feel better. For a while.

But it was different in the office now. Bud Horne and he planned little things like fouling up letters or putting foolish tabs on the desk or swiping cigars. That was a funny one. The chaplain knew they took them. He never said a word—just opening a fresh box every day and leaving it there. Now the fun was going out of taking them.

They wished that Father Hyland would go to Albany, but something always seemed to turn up, an epidemic in the infirmary or a man wanting to get himself baptized at the State Hospital. Still they had their fun.

Last Sunday, at Mass, Bill Martin had played a postlude and the rather raucous choir he had supposedly trained had grinned widely. He played it very slowly and solemnly, so that it sounded churchy, sort of, only it was "Flat Foot Floogie with a Floy Floy."

That had backfired. When the priest had finished unvesting he had come down to the wheezy little organ, made Bill push over, and had said, "That postlude you played—it ought to go like this." And he sure played it with a *floy-floy*. He knew his songs, all right. But he wasn't supposed to, was he? He knew too much.

And what was this act he was putting on about building a church? He hadn't even gone to Albany yet. And then he did go.

Ambrose Hyland had waited until the plans were mature in his mind and until he was positive of the co-operation of Mr. Bay and Rabbi Schoenkopf. He was surprised, in fact, by the enthusiasm of their endorsements. He had letters from them, and he read and studied their arguments for the three churches as his train stopped at Ticonderoga. Deliberately, he did not even look out the window.

For the rest of the trip he marshaled his thoughts. He did not anticipate any difficulty with his co-religionists; certainly they would perceive the necessity of having Christ present. Their only objections would be practical, but for these he had an answer. It was good penology. It was written by Alexander Patterson, His Majesty's Commissioner of Prisons for England and Wales. He had memorized it:

It seems that greater regard is still paid (in America) to the physical and material welfare of a prisoner than to his moral and spiritual needs. This is reflected in the expense, thought, and time devoted to the care of the body, compared with that spent on the training of character. Hospitals are built and equipped regardless of expense, the equal of any in the state or city. Yet the prisoners are not sent to prison for prolonged medical or surgical repair, but that their characters may be straightened and strengthened. Is anything like the amount spent on prison hospitals available for the building of churches and chapels in a prison where men may worship in a place set aside for the purpose, rather than in an auditorium redolent of lectures, songs, and cinemas?

How aptly that fitted his case! Anybody with sense could see that such an abuse must be remedied.

Confidently, he met Mr. Arnold Colpoys in Albany.

He sat in the overstuffed office, talking, watching this un-bending man. He had known a portly gentleman on the golf links, a good fellow, stopping at eleven to remember departed Elks, a papal knight, father of a seminarian. But he had never met the politician before.

When he had finished, Mr. Colpoys said, "I hope you under-stand my position. I'm a Catholic. We're always being accused of interfering with the state. I'm not the man to back you."

"Mr. Bay—Rabbi Schoenkopf did."

"They can. I can't."

"Why can't you? I expected you to."

"Why?"

"Because you believe in the Blessed Sacrament."

"That isn't the point."

"What is the point?"

"That you can't build a denominational church on state prop-erty. That's all there is to it."

"I see." And the chaplain saw all too clearly.

"Look. I'll compromise with you. Mr. Mulrooney will not endorse anything he thinks is un-American. If he gives you the green light, I'll see what I can do."

Thinking over Mr. Colpoys's words on his way up the hill to the commissioner's office, Father Hyland kept remembering that he had been promised nothing. "I'll see what I can do." That was politicians' double-talk. It meant exactly nothing. Did he have to sell the Catholics the idea that God could do what no human agency could do? He had not even used that argument; he had taken it for granted.

It was an argument that had worked with Allan Green, a simple boy in prison, but it would not work with the sophis-ticates outside. In a way, rough as they were, his men were better. Allan Green had looked up at him, his eyes trusting, when he told him that the secret of working hard at his own defense lay really in leaving the issue up to God. It had meant something. Oh yes. Greeney had moments of darkness—hours when he was unsure. And the weak word, impatience, did not do justice to the agony of waiting, to the frustration of delay, which men knew in prison. But, fundamentally, Greeney had faith. And what the constant reception of the Sacraments and a church to pray in could mean to a boy like that, and to thousands of others, anyone should be able to see. Certainly he must make the commissioner see.

He had been more forcible with Commissioner Mulrooney than he had intended to be, but he thought that he had made his point. He had stressed the moral rehabilitation of the men, the therapeutic value of religion. He had underlined the necessity of the three churches as a truly American way of worship. He had reminded the commissioner that his office was one of correction, not of detention.

The commissioner seemed sympathetic. "I'd give it to you tomorrow if I could," he said, "but that's not in my jurisdiction."

"Why not, Mr. Commissioner? Why isn't it?"

"Look, Father—here's what you asked for. You have no land, no money, no materials, no labor, no precedent. You are exposing us to all kinds of difficulties. If you use your prisoners on the construction, you'll put escape hazards in their hands and you'll have the union down on us. If you introduce a denominational church on government property, you'll have all kinds of fanatics ganging up on us. It's too big for me, Father."

"It's not too big for God. Let's see. What did you say we needed?"

"Everything. Labor, money, materials, land, the governor's sanction. I'm sorry. You just haven't got anything."

"Except faith. I'll get the governor's sanction. Then I'll provide the labor and the materials and the money. All we need from you is the land. Will you give us that?"

"All right. If you get those other things, I'll see what I can do."

Father Hyland turned to go. He thought, *"I'll see what I can do!"* The same formula. Nothing that could not be retracted tomorrow.

"Just a minute, Father," the commissioner called after him.

"If you're going to see the governor, you might stress the idea of rehabilitation a little more. He's following Al Smith pretty much. It's good too."

"Thanks for the tip."

"I'm all for rehabilitation myself, of course," the commissioner added slowly, "but sometimes you wonder if any of these men ever make good. Once a thief, always a thief." He paused again. "Did you ever know one of them who was saved?"

"One."

"Really stopped stealing?"

"No. He remained a thief right up to the end."

"I don't get it."

Father Hyland, knowing how little it would mean, quoted Saint Chrysostom on the Good Thief, "This thief stole salvation from the Cross and made the kingdom of heaven his plunder."

The commissioner looked baffled. "Good luck with the governor," he mumbled.

Afterward Father Hyland was not sure whether he had had good luck with the governor or not. Mr. Lehman had seemed to be more receptive than the others, but who could tell? Father Hyland had made one point that seemed to strike home.

"So we have seven hundred men in the idle companies. That means they can't work. Mr. Mulrooney proposed the lack of workmen as a difficulty. I suggest it as a solution—to your idle population. Suppose they're not skilled. We could teach them, couldn't we? That would help."

"Yes." The governor smiled. "I can think of certain criticisms we've had. But they forget the depression."

"That's what makes Dannemora horrible. No work."

"I know. It's a good point. Still, there's unemployment outside."

"You'll consider giving us land, then?"

"Yes. I'll consider it."

"Look, Mr. Lehman," the priest said at last, "do you mean you will just consider it, or will you do something about it?"

The governor smiled again. "You wouldn't be putting pressure on me, would you?"

"Oh, I suppose I am. But it gets pretty discouraging—this runaround all the time. Nobody says anything. They seem to think it's a crazy scheme. It isn't!"

"I don't think it is. Only you'd better work it out a little more."

"How much more? What else can I do?"

"You need backing. Lots of it."

"Where can I get it? Who's behind me? Where do I go next?"

"Go everywhere, Father. Talk. Lecture. See people. Get around. Then come back to me."

"All right," he said. "I will. But—man to man—are you with me?"

"Man to man," the governor said, stressing the words, "I am."

So Father Hyland began. In the next couple of days he thought he had seen everybody in Albany. From his hotel room in the De Witt he sent out scores of letters, offering his services, gratis if necessary, to women's clubs and men's sodalities, every place that would listen to a speaker. But mainly he interviewed people, until he knew all the rebuttals by heart, and began to wish these people would think up some new objections. The old, answered ones became so monotonous.

And who was in back of him? Now that he was on his way home to Dannemora, he wondered who was supporting him. One, he could be sure of. His last letter had been to Mother Angela in her Carmel, telling her of all the discouragement, all the need. "You," he had written, "must get us a church. *You.*" He underscored it, *"have direct wires to heaven."*

He had her support. And in the prison only one man, certainly. When he got back he would ask Max Bergner for prayers. The only one he could be sure of.

And all the way on the train from Albany, while reading his breviary, he heard the same patter of objection, the phrases dinned into him through his interviews: don't be taken in by

prisoners—they'll use you for everything—they've fooled simple priests into getting paroles for them—dangers of the parole
system—coddling convicts—the smart ones don't get caught—
don't get fooled—every single one says he was framed—everyone in there claims to be innocent——

He finished the breviary and turned, for escape, to a detective story. In fiction everything was so nice and clear. The evil
man was proven guilty, and swift reprisal came upon him. He
was sent to jail or hanged. That was the solution. No loose
ends. No problem of rehabilitation or spiritualization—no need
for a church.

Even under the nice, clipped formula of the detective story
he could hear it—

Every single one says he was framed.

Everyone in there claims to be innocent.

Don't get fooled.

Don't get fooled.

There is no hope for them.

5.   In his cell at eight-thirty that November night, when the
silent time started and the only means of communication was
through the little boxes filled with notes strung on cord trolleys
from one cell to another, Greeney knew.

It was hopeless. He had passed tabs that way to so many
men down the cell block. He had come to know so many, not
intimately, for that would never happen, but well enough.
There was plenty of talk. But it didn't make sense. He knew
now.

It was hopeless. Everybody he had talked to, sent tabs to,
was innocent. Everybody was framed. There wasn't a guilty
guy on the cell block—this or any other. Everyone had been
given a dirty deal.

God, what could you do? How could you get anybody to
believe you hadn't done it, when every single one claimed to
be innocent? How would you break that down?

But he was innocent! There must be some jerks in here who
were just caught red-handed, guilty, admitting it. Weren't

there? Just one would help. But all around him in the quiet before lights-out were men working on their cases. Finding something, anything, desperately, never with resignation, always with a hope of proof, of someone's confession on the outside.

He'd better work on his own case. He got out the records which he had, already soiled at the creases, and started to read them again. They were just words. They didn't mean anything. They got to mean something.

Oh, God in heaven, make them, please, mean something! Prove I was framed! Prove it, God!

One of the little communication boxes stopped at his cell. He reached out for it, read what it contained. It was barracks-room humor. At first he wanted to crumple it up, and the words of prayer were still underlying his thinking, but then it struck him funny, and he laughed and sent the box on to the next cell.

After that he spent his time trying to remember a story the men might not have heard.

At eight-thirty, when the order was given, Tom Riordan stood up from the circle of heavy chairs which lined the guarded hall everyone in the State Hospital called "The Board of Directors' Room." The conversations here were more profound, more elevated than in other parts of the compound.

As usual, one man refused to go, and the guards were lifting him forcibly out of his chair. He was saying, "I am Christ. I will tell you when to go. You will not tell me." His bearded face, tortured, white, peered out of the gathering blackness like a Greek Christus from an icon.

Religious bugs. Every one of them. No wonder, Tom thought, depressed, that any sign of religion was met with cynicism and would be taken as a symptom of madness.

He had not understood this at first. When the guards had sneered at him for kneeling down to say his prayers at night, when the psychologist had probed him mercilessly about his religious practices and their possible connection with sins

against the sixth commandment, and when even the inmates
had made nasty remarks when he went off to Sunday Mass,
he had thought that it was all part of a plan to undermine
faith. But now he knew. He was one of many suspected of
religious delusions. He was classified. His love of God was a
thing to make him dangerous. He was watched.

Another night was coming. He must listen to words rising
from broken sleep and from shattered dreams, pious ejacula-
tions booming into blasphemy. All night. What could he do?

He had been happy that day. In the small cubicle which
Father Hyland had procured for him to start his library. In
the large trash barrel, filled with old books and pamphlets, he
had found something called "Happiness or Holiness." It was
an appeal for membership in the Third Order of St. Francis,
for laymen who would dedicate themselves to the service of
God according to the Franciscan rule.

He read it avidly, but then he knew it was not for him. He
was a murderer, among the criminal insane. The Church held
no place for him. Even if he should be released—impossible, of
course. The Church had a place for women, the Magdalenes
of the Good Shepherd, but no place for grown men. Besides,
could he stay in the state of grace long enough?

He still had evil thoughts, hateful, revengeful. He must put
this holy dream out of his mind.

Now, kneeling in prayer, the desire and frustration were full
upon him again. How could he dedicate his life to God? The
jeers around him reminded him of what he was in all eyes—a
religious bug. He could do nothing except hold on to the one
thing left.

Last Sunday after Mass Father Hyland had asked the "altar
boys" their names, the other men first. Then he turned to
Tom.

"You're somebody too," he had said.

To one man in the world, Tom Riordan thought, he was not
a number. He was Tom Riordan, and Tom Riordan must
serve God now, in his own way. Even here. He was somebody,
wasn't he?

In the idle-company tier Max Bergner was giving these two hours to preparation for prayer. When the lights went out he could kneel on the stone floor, compose himself, not physically but mentally, as the spiritual books advised, and let God send the thoughts. Not even thoughts, sometimes, but the known presence of God all around him. When this came, as it did more often of late, he would pass the whole night and no one would see him except the guards. They did not bother him, kneeling upright on the stone of the cell, and eventually, because of his union with God, he would be unaware of them. Then the night was too short, since he had been granted this way of prayer, to make ready for Holy Communion.

If he had any petition at all it was not for himself but for what Father Hyland had told him to pray for—that these others also might have a chance to go to Communion every day. He had not said anything, but he was offering all penance, all prayer, all union with God, in his own way, just as one individual, that his Father's church might rise in Dannemora.

In Philadelphia, Mother Angela and her community were offering their nightly vigil in the Carmelite monastery for the same intention.

CHAPTER SIX

In the weeks that remained before Christmas, Ambrose Hyland had little time to do anything except his prison work. However, he did manage to squeeze in a few lectures in surrounding towns. Each prison day now provided him with further material. He found his lecture audiences interested enough in prison work, particularly if his stories dealt with notorious inmates such as Lucky Luciano, but the majority of people seemed to have no very great enthusiasm for the redemption of convicts. "Lock them up and keep them there," seemed to be their motto.

It was a particularly popular attitude in those days and it did not help the inmates' Christmas spirit to know that the press was conducting a campaign against what it called "coddling prisoners." In his talks Father Hyland attempted to show what was behind this, but he knew that one would have to have access to the prisoners' lives, such as only he had, to understand the new wave of bitterness which swept over them.

Yes. They were idle. But was there a premium on doing nothing for three hundred and sixty-five days a year? Nothing, except having it rubbed into them that it didn't matter whether they worked or not? No one wanted their work. A few men, working cotton on outmoded looms. The rest, nothing. Their arms ached. The poisons stayed in them.

"What do you want me to do?"

"Sit here and rot."

"Until I die. Until I go over the walls—stir crazy——"

There were about two thousand inmates in the prison proper; there were twelve hundred in the adjoining State Hospital, gone mad from confinement and idleness.

And the priest knew that he alone had the solution. With no State budget for occupational therapy what was there to let him put it into effect?

He saw the dilemma clearly. If he had the money, they might give him permission to build; if he had permission to build, he might get the money. But who would make the first move?

He discovered another thing. He himself was without power. He could recommend, interview, plead, cajole. But there was scarcely one thing in which he could command and expect his order to be carried out. Here he was tolerated.

It was no wonder, he thought, considering his own helplessness and the fact that no official evaluation had ever been put upon the prison chaplain's function, that the inmates' attitude toward him had not changed. He had promised them a church, with a magnificent gesture, and they knew, as they knew everything within the walls, that he was getting nowhere. Of course, as in so many other matters, their expectations were often unreasonable, and even the new men like Greeney had

sunk into sullen antipathy once they had discovered that he
could not say "sesame" and swing open the gates.

The myth of Father Booth grew during those days; he could
do anything; this new chaplain just talked. And what would
he do for Christmas?

The thought of Christmas was an irony to him. With Tom
Riordan's help he had prepared a program for the hospital and
the plan of decoration, if garish, was at least bright. But for the
prison itself—he looked around the auditorium—poinsettias,
holly, pine branches, even a small crib—everything was mockery. Since the coming of winter even the altar itself was im-
periled by a leak in the roof directly over it.

He asked Joe Hogan, "What did Father Booth do for
Christmas?"

"Oh—pretty well. He gave every man a little gift."

"Every man? Three thousand men?"

"Mu-humm. I don't know how—but he did it."

"Then we'll have to do it too—somehow."

He thought desperately of the contributions he had received
for his lectures, pitifully small, and of how he had hoped that
they would be the nucleus of the church building fund. He
studied his own bank account and wiped it out with a signature. His mother, brother, sister, a few friends, gave what they
could.

He thought then of Joe Madden in New York. He had
heard that Madden's Restaurant gave a Christmas party every
year, the proceeds of which went toward various charities.
Desperately he wrote him, but he had no reply until two days
before Christmas.

Then great packing cases bulked up in the storeroom, filled
with oranges. Together with his sullen staff he got three thousand paper bags filled with fruit and candy within the next
forty-eight hours and had them delivered to the cells. It wasn't
much, he knew, but it was something.

Christmas morning dawned raw and sodden, with the snow
rotting under a drizzling rain. He had said early Mass at the
hospital and that had been right enough, with Tom Riordan

serving and an improvised choir of inmates drowned out by the terrific basso of an attendant who roared out the "Adeste."

His second Mass was in the prison infirmary. He stopped on the way out and smiled at an old man whom they had wheeled in in a chair. The priest could not bring himself to say, "Merry Christmas." He could only smile.

"Did you get your package?" he asked.

"Yeah. I got it."

"How was it?"

"My oranges was rotten."

"Oh no!" It was a cry of dismay. "I'll send you another."

"Don't bother. You sent the good ones to West Hall. We got the lousy ones."

It was not true, but what was the use of saying so? He went on silently.

The roof was leaking more than ever. Dominic and he rigged up an awning over the altar so that, they hoped, the rain would not seep down on the oblations, but it only served to convert the drops into a drizzle. As the auditorium began to fill and the heat of bodies raised the temperature to unbearable heights, the seepage turned into steam.

Now, from the kitchen below, fumes began to rise, thickening the atmosphere still more. It might be Christmas dinner, but it certainly was cauliflower and onions and undefinable spices mingling with the smell of bodies, of old clothes, of dirty socks, vaporizing in the thickening atmosphere, turning odor into taste.

Before the consecration the priest thought he was about to be sick. He held on through the silent Mass. Unaccountably, Bill Martin had decided not to play the organ, and the singers had stood there, ready with Christmas hymns, and then, looking sheepish, had retreated into anonymous ranks.

When the Mass was over he was tempted to escape, but instead he went from cell to cell, the dark, narrow ones in the old blocks, the black ones in Segregation, to all who could not or would not come to Mass. He did not say, "Merry Christmas." He said, "God bless you!"

"The candy stuck to my oranges."

"He got four pieces. I got three."

"Padre Booth gave wool socks."

Silence.

At last he was through. He realized that he had had no coffee and was still fasting. That was why he felt such pain in the pit of his stomach. He would be better when he had some food. But he was not hungry.

He drove fast to Chateaugay. Of course his mother was waiting for him, her hands full of flour from the kitchen.

For the first time that day his voice, with an effort, was cheerful and bright. "Merry Christmas!"

She looked at him. She said, " 'Merry Christmas, bah,' said Tiny Tim. Come in out of the rain. We'll have fourteen for dinner today, like old times. And here, drink this coffee. Be careful, it's hot. You look like the wreck of the *Hesperus*. Merry Christmas, Ambrose."

2. Lee Sapis Robinson remembered, that Christmas, that he had never been free. There was nothing in this place. Not even work for him. He wasn't smart enough to escape. He had tried that.

He sucked at his orange. Every Sunday he had been going to Mass for the Catholics and he had heard the sermons about heaven and hell and how all the souls on earth were in prison but would escape someday into glory. Today he had been to Christmas Mass there in the reeking auditorium, and for him the place had been changed into a cathedral with the lights and the flowers, the Christmas decorations, and the beautiful clothing of the priest. Yet they said it was only a promise of things to come.

"There is a lovely land, far, far away."

So he began his plan.

That night he would start with the little nail file they had not found on him yet, and he would file away a bit of bedspring, cut off an inch of his sock, let the filings drop into it.

No. He was not foolish. Other men would not think of this

way. He would twist a little of the bedspring off and let it fall into the inch of rag torn from his sock.

Lee Sapis Robinson had his own way out.

3. The place which had at first filled him with horror was where he found most consolation. As the patients at the State Hospital assumed personalities, he found in them a simplicity, even a sweetness, totally different from the grim attitudes of the prison. It got so that he looked forward to the two days a week that he spent with them.

There was Pegleg Connell who always came for an interview.

"I want you should write my aunt, Mrs. Glendenning of Oyster Bay. She don't answer my letters. I read in the society column that she was pouring at tea. I wish the top of the kettle would fall on her foot and scald her."

"No, you don't, Pegleg."

"No, I don't. But I wish she'd write."

Father Hyland did not tell him that he had already written Mrs. Glendenning of Oyster Bay who said that she had never heard of Pegleg Connell but that she certainly would pray for him.

"Maybe she will write someday. Who knows?"

"It doesn't matter. Now what was I here for?"

"To go to confession?"

"I suppose that was it, but if you want to know, it's about the same as it was last week, *and not very much* improvement. Now what do I have to do?"

"You'd better get down on your knees."

"Don't delay me. It's practically mess hour."

But Pegleg knelt down and went to confession.

There was God who came in to impart his blessing, not to be blessed. There was old Tony who simply smiled and went out again. He had not spoken for fourteen years. There was Raoul, who would destroy the sun if the men did not do what Father Hyland wanted. And Tim, each week, presented him with his personal check for a million dollars.

There was one dark boy who had been diagnosed as having a complication of epilepsy and St. Vitus's dance. A queer case, that.

Afterward he would go through the wards, stop by the bedsides of the very old, who would reach out with withered hands toward him and cling to him as long as he would stay and follow him with almost sightless eyes as he went about. Then he would go down the long corridors of beds and through the sections where the restrained patients were. One man in particular always smiled at him. The priest wondered why they restrained him, until one day, just as he turned his back, the patient kicked out wickedly at the slop bucket which was at his feet, aiming it directly at the priest. When Father Hyland turned, the face, still bland and smiling, emerged out of the strapped canvas bag.

Back in the little library which he had fixed up for Tom Riordan the priest would conduct an instruction class, giving the rudiments of religion to men who had rarely heard the name of God except in blasphemy. This class was composed of the better patients, and some of them, young boys, showed no symptoms of madness at all. Not until you knew them well. Then you could see it. The suicide slashes on the wrist. One day the fever, next time the dullness.

Yet, whatever their condition, he knew that he was helping them, which was more than he could say for the convicts in the prison.

In only one man had he never seen the slightest trace of insanity. That was Tom Riordan. One day he asked him directly.

"I'm homicidal," he said. "I want to kill people."

"You don't kill them, Tom."

"Not now. I killed a man once."

"That was years ago—outside."

"I could do it again."

"But you don't. What stops you?"

"You do, Father."

The priest stood up hurriedly and took his two black bags.

"Thanks, Tom," he said. "Thanks."

On the way up the street toward his boardinghouse, past the walls of the prison where the snow lay on the sidewalks, and in front of the warden's castle where it had been swept away, Father Hyland kept telling himself that he must not allow himself to become emotional. Whenever he did, which was not often, there was this pain. He felt it now, biting into him. He was glad when he heard Warden Murphy's cheerful voice calling down to him.

"Come up here, Padre! I've got good news for you." It was a respite. His two bags were growing heavy. He turned and started up the stairs.

"Good Lord, man, what's the matter with you?"

"Nothing," the priest said. "Just tired, I guess."

"It gave me a shock to see you. You're all gray. Come in and sit down. Say—how many pounds have you lost?"

"A few. I—I'm reducing." He laughed at the idea. "And the rest is prison pallor, I suppose."

"Take it easy, man, or we won't have you around."

"Is that important?"

"Oh, come on. We can't have you feel that way. You're the one has got to be cheerful."

"I am."

"Sure—you're better now you've given up the fancy idea of a church."

"I what? Gave up what?"

"That church of yours. Haven't you given it up?"

All he could say was, "No."

"O.K." The warden shook his head at him. Then he smiled. "I suppose if it's going to kill you, I'd better get it for you."

"You mean that?"

"When I look at you, I want to say yes. Well, anyway—get yourself some money and I'll see what I can do."

"Can I quote you to the bishop?"

"Well—I don't know about that. It's risky. God knows what you'll say. But go ahead. I'll chance it. Just tell him I have some land in mind."

"That's enough."

"Say—you look better already."

"I feel better. You said you had good news. You certainly had!"

"Not what I had in mind at all. It was something else."

"I don't want anything else in the world."

"Whether you do or not, you'll get it. Can you take a walk with me? I'll carry your bags."

Together the two men went out the side door, through the warden's snow-filled garden, past the greenhouse, and across the street. There, under four great trees, foliaged with shining snow in the sunset, was a little white cottage. The warden went up to the door and swung it open. Inside, to the right, Father Hyland could see a grand piano, remarkably like his own at Chateaugay—and the furniture, too, looked like his. But certainly. Around the walls were family pictures, and several of himself in all stages of his career, as a boy actor in the high-school play, as a student at Catholic university, as a young priest newly ordained, as a professor at the seminary, and as a curate, standing before the beautiful church at Ticonderoga, proud and smiling. Someone had got them from somewhere. His first impression was that he must take them down at once!

Then there was a distraction—a rustling from the inner room.

Comfortable in an easy chair his mother sat, reading a newspaper. She looked up at him over the top of it and said casually, "Welcome home, Ambrose."

"I'll be going," the warden said, putting down the black bags. "I thought you'd need a place, so here it is. Now see you get some rest."

And after he had gone and mother and son had made an excited inventory of the tiny house, even to planning how a back nook could be a chapel so that, if the bishop allowed, the Blessed Sacrament could be reserved, Ambrose Hyland decided to rest.

As soon as he sat down, the doorbell rang. A woman entered, talking all in one unbroken and unbreakable sentence, explaining that she was Mrs. Daniel Cassidy, and did he know how her husband was doing, and there wasn't a finer man than himself in the world when he wasn't in drink, and would he look at the pictures of the three lovely children, and was there anything he could do to get Danno out, with him not to blame at all, such as a small note now, to the D.A. and the judge, or wouldn't it be better to go to the governor and if it wouldn't be too much trouble to drop a line to all the jurymen because they had misunderstood, or if that wasn't any use, and who could tell at all, at least he could write to the pastor, a monsignor and all in Brooklyn, saying he saw no reason why since it wasn't her fault at all, she couldn't belong to the Altar and Rosary Society, and just add a bit telling him that the girl should be taken into the parochial, where there was no room for all the children, because it was better for her there, with her father in trouble, than in the P.S., not that she wanted to be beholden, mind you, and could take care of herself and all, and it was luck that she found out where the priest's new cottage was, and wasn't it nice, though she had a nice flat herself, though she shouldn't be saying so, and if he could just put in a word about how Dan Cassidy was regular at his Christian duties, as she knew without hearing he was, it wouldn't hurt at all, and wasn't the priest lucky to have such a fine man as Dan working side by side with him?

Then after the supper had been reheated and his mother and he had begun to talk about old times, one of the two telephones rang. It was the pastor in the local church who wanted to know if Father Hyland could come down for an hour or so to hear confessions.

When he got back at nine-thirty, the house was full, with his brother and sister and their families, and he got on famously with the youngsters. Mary said it was too bad he would never have any of his own, and he replied that he had three thousand, and believe me they were pretty childish sometimes.

So at midnight he went to bed. At one-thirty the phone rang to say that a man was dying in the infirmary, but there was no hurry. He could tend to him in the morning—whereupon he dressed hastily, went down again to the village church, got the Blessed Sacrament and the oils, anointed the man, and stayed with him until it was time for Mass.

And the warden was sure, as he said to his wife, that now the padre had his little home, he could get some rest. That was all he needed.

4. Brendon O'Malley was still at divinity school in Seattle, but he was all mixed up, and the spring was a restlessness in him. There could not be anything more beautiful than the skies, and he was grounded. Such skies were over Spain, and there was fighting there and he could be in it.

Yet which side would you be on? At the Catholic Seamen's Club they told him one thing, and everyone else said the other. Most of the time he thought Franco was wrong, but you couldn't be sure, because while the rebels were bombing little children, real little children in hospitals, the loyalists were shooting at a statue of a mother and child—a Virgin and Child.

He couldn't get it clear in his head. It was bad to kill children in a bombing, but you didn't mean to do that. It was war and children died. But if you destroyed the Mother and Child you took them from children yet unborn, and you were not just destroying a statue; it was faith that was being destroyed. And that was deliberate.

How could you tell?

He tried to forget. That spring he trained a children's choir and their voices went up beyond the spires into the skies from which dropped no bombs upon the figures of Mother and Child.

But still he wanted to fight.

Did it matter on which side?

They were both wrong. . . .

5. In his prayers, Max Bergner had a new devotion, a name which he had never heard in the litanies, and he called now

upon Our Lady of Ransom, for Father Hyland had said in his sermon last Sunday that outside the prison also all men were convicted of sin, from which Our Lady, through her Son, could free them.

He would pray to her, and she would pray to Him, and somewhere upon a cross, nailed there like the thieves with Christ, one soul would rise up into heaven, ransomed that moment, in Paradise like the good thief.

Now he tried to see things through the priest's eyes, and as he prayed the symbol grew. It was a Gothic church. It towered over a prison wall. Its spires escaped into heaven.

6.   A week later the old bishop was determined to be crusty. He liked this young man, Ambrose Hyland, but it would never do to have visionary schemes all over his diocese. He was getting old and he needed things shipshape for his successor.

The bishop did not care about the money. It was merely the idea of the thing. He wouldn't give one red cent to this church in a prison until he knew what was up. That business at Ticonderoga, now—forty thousand dollars for redecoration. Of course it had turned the old church into a handsome edifice.

"Look here," he said. "You've got another scheme—and you're not going to have a cathedral at Dannemora. I've got a list of things you did at Ticonderoga. Look here! Altar rail, baptismal font—all right; a job on the organ—I suppose; and let's see—rood screen, carpets for the predella, Gothic vestments, Anglican surplices for the choir—Anglican, indeed!"

"Benedictine, Your Excellency."

"Same thing. Albs without lace. What did you do with the lace that was there? Never mind answering that. And oh yes, a new bishop's throne. I hope that means what I don't think it does—a new throne for the old bishop. And so now you want to do that all over again."

"Not quite, Your Excellency. I just want a church—a place for the Blessed Sacrament."

"You can keep it in your new house."

"Can I? May I do that?"

"Well, since I said it, I suppose so. But that isn't the question. What kind of backing have you got on this thing anyhow?"

"The warden said he would try to get me some land if I had the money."

"So the first idea for money popped into your head was from your bishop. Why didn't you go to that cousin of yours you admire so much—that monsignor fellow in New York, there—what's his name—Keegan—Keenan—eh?"

"May I, Your Excellency?"

"Now hold on. You're not getting around me that way."

"All I really want from you is permission to solicit funds."

"Is that all now? And you'd refuse this?" He held out a check for five hundred dollars which he had already made out. "I thought maybe you wouldn't. It's the last you'll get out of me, though. Just a drop in the bucket. Will you take it?"

"Gladly, Bishop. If permission to build goes with it."

The wrinkles around the tired old eyes turned up in a smile. "Yes, permission goes with it, if you get the land and the material and the governor's signature and all you need. Otherwise, spend it next Christmas. I heard about that. But if you get your church I want an account of every rood screen and laceless alb that goes into it."

"Of course. And one thing more."

"Don't push me too far now."

"Just this. May I solicit contributions from the other bishops of the archdiocese?"

The bishop burst into laughter. "Yes! That'll be good. And if you get anything from them they can't go around saying what an old fool I was."

The bishop was still laughing when the young priest knelt to kiss his ring. "God bless you, boy," he was saying. "The luck of God go with you. Go out and grab all the money you can. And say, by the way, who's the patron of this church of yours, anyway?"

"Saint Dismas, the Good Thief."

"That's wonderful! How did you ever think of that one?

That's perfect. The Good Thief, indeed," and the laughter of his bishop rang in his memory all the way to New York and to Monsignor Keegan's.

They talked that day, the monsignor and he, and together they built a church in Dannemora, spire and all. For the first time since he had come to his decision, the younger priest found a man who did not think his plan was visionary, who approved it from the beginning, and was ready with help.

"Tomorrow," the monsignor said, "you spend all day writing a letter to the bishops. You're in luck, you see. The next day they're meeting here with the cardinal. Have the letter ready for me—don't make it too heavy—and I'll present it. Stand by, yourself, if the cardinal wants to see you. I think he may."

Then, for the first time, he himself was the devil's advocate. "And suppose after all this the governor says no. I only have a half-promise of Warden Murphy's to go on."

"Ambrose," his cousin said solemnly, "that thought wouldn't have crossed your mind if you hadn't been hungry. Where do you want to go?"

"I'd like to go to a place on Fifty-sixth Street—Joe Madden's."

"Whew!"

"Isn't it all right?"

"Sure it's all right. But it's pretty sporty. How did you know about it?"

"Joe Madden sent up crates of oranges for Christmas. I'd like to thank him."

"You'd like to meet him too. He's a character."

Together they went to Joe Madden's. Father Hyland had very little impression of the place, he was so taken up with its proprietor. When he heard who he was, Joe put his hearing aid on as if to listen, and then shouted at everybody to keep still. He always put the aid on when he talked and took it off when he was supposed to be listening.

"Hey, youse guys!" he bellowed. "This is the padre from Dannemora. Get it? Steaks are a buck more tonight. I know I gyp you anyhow, but this dough is going to a good thief. Ask me no questions! Come on or I'll bat you down."

The crowd loved it. They were flashy-dressed, gold-toothed, wide-grinning. They were big spenders, sportsmen.

"Come on, part with your ill-gotten gains!" Joe was shouting. "One of youse guys pass the hat. And this ain't church! I don't want to hear your money clink. I want it should rustle."

It rustled. When he left, Father Hyland had a sizable wad of bills.

"I knock 'em down—you drag 'em out," Joe called after him.

Father Hyland smiled at the monsignor. "I know what you meant," he said, "when I proposed Joe Madden's."

"What did I say?"

"You said, 'Whew!' That's the only adequate expression."

Then the next day he was in the mood to write a letter to the bishops, perfectly respectful, but not too heavy—the light touch. He laughed as the implication of the phrase came to him—the light *touch*.

He knew that it would work. He knew the cardinal would see him, and was prepared with what he would say.

"And so I am asking for further contributions."

"Do I give you contributions?"

"Oh yes, Your Eminence. Many."

"Many?"

"They take the form of black sheep from New York."

"Oh. I see. Your—parishioners."

"Yes, Your Eminence. But you know, you expect me to perform a miracle."

"Do I really?"

"Yes, really. You expect me to convert them into woolly white lambs. And with what?"

His Eminence laughed. "With this, for instance?"

He held out a check. It was for five thousand dollars. And Father Hyland knew why they called this man "The Cardinal of Charity."

But it was true. Here in New York—somewhere about this city—were his parishioners—men to come to him. But these men would not have a nothingness, they would have a possibility of redemption, these new, black sheep.

If the governor approved.

7.   In Greenwich Village that spring night Carlos Santa Cruz saw the girl. It was unseasonably warm, and he had left the Pepper Pot at about one and was strolling aimlessly down toward MacDougall Street. She came around a corner, walking swiftly, carrying a sketch pad. In the light of the street lamp he saw her. For the first time in his life he was shy.

He might have forgotten everything except a splash of red hair, a bravely cloven chin. But a half-hour later he came across her again, at the far northwest corner of Washington Square. Suddenly, angularly, she stopped and sat on a bench. Even sitting, she seemed poised for flight. Other girls would be crying.

Carlos stopped before her. He seemed to be talking to himself.

"I, too, am an artist. I, too, cannot paint. But tonight I have seen someone whom I would like as my model—my inspiration. I would not paint her with flowers like pretty girls in calendars. I would make her strong—a woman. I would make her The Woman."

He paused. The girl's face, planed, angular, her coppery hair, came fully into view. "I would want her to pose for me," Carlos added.

The girl looked straight ahead. "Not tonight."

"No. Not tonight."

"Not any night."

"No. Only in the strong sun."

"Yes."

"We will meet at Ruffino's at eleven." It was a command.

"Yes."

"Good night, Madonna."

8.   In the outer library the four automatons were at work. A stack of mail to be answered lay beside each desk, and Bud

Horne's typewriter went on. Pete did not ride the carriage that morning. He was in his cage.

From the inner office subdued voices were barely audible. Interviews. The thousand stories, going on and on. The chaplain listening, making notes, more wearily now.

At last Bill Martin stopped work. The other three typewriters continued.

"I had a dream last night."

"... *wishes to thank you for your kind contribution,* ..." Bud Horne typed. "Yeah?"

"... *advised you that he has contacted the New York Diocesan Charitable Bureau in your behalf* ..." Cassidy typed. "I never dream."

"... *will be glad to see you when you come to visit your son* ..." Dominic typed. "What was it?"

"I dreamt we got a church."

"Dreams go by contraries," Cassidy said.

"You're getting nuts like the boss," Dominic said.

"I suppose there was an organ in it," Bud Horne said.

"Yes," Bill Martin replied. "There was."

"And you was playing it?"

"Yes, I was."

"You're screwy."

Then the yard mail came. There was a yellow telegram which Bud Horne tore open. He did not show it to the others. He stuck it under the chaplain's door where he could find it if he looked for it.

It read, "Church plan approved. Have site designated by Warden Murphy."

It was signed by the governor.

CHAPTER SEVEN

The prison population gave no sign during the long, hot summer that its attitude toward the chaplain had altered. The talk was about the change in the haircut rule, and they were glad they could choose their own style and they were still morose about the press attacks. They wished that someone would do something about them and blamed the padre because he did not. Since they did not hear his lectures, they continued to say that he would not help them with legal questions, though they had to admit that he was good about family assistance. And they knew he was ill. Anyone could see that.

So it went on. The summer brought more checks to the office. The warden had staked out the place, high on the hill, where the silo and barns stood. And the priest resolved to stay on until he could clear ground and dig. After that he would see a doctor. Not yet.

He had the plans for the church stretched out before him every day in the office and looked at them, studied them, in the infrequent moments at noontime when the men were at lunch and he was not, because food hurt him now. Besides, he could study the plans.

He had gone to Washington to get them, asking advice at the university. They recommended his old college friend Bob Weppinger at the office of Frederick V. Murphy.

"He's the best," they said.

He must have been. He took one look at Father Hyland and remarked, "Oh, I know what you want. You did the work with Rambush at Ticonderoga."

He unrolled some sketches. "Like this," he added. "I remember you had taste. These are a little simple, but they're for country churches, you see."

"How much would this one come to?"

"I guess you could put that up for half a million. Maybe a little more."

"I see." Father Hyland rolled up the sketch.

"How much money do you have?"

"Exactly six thousand one hundred and fourteen dollars and no cents."

Bob Weppinger coughed. "I thought—— You see I know what you spent at Ticonderoga."

"So did the bishop. But this is different. We'll have our own labor. My boys will build it."

A light came into the architect's eyes. "You mean—really build it?"

"Why, yes."

"What about material?"

"I have an old prison wall in mind. We can tear it down and use the stone."

"How about tools? Structural steel—girders and such?"

"Not many tools—and no steel. Escape hazards, you know."

"Wonderful! No steel! Just stone. Personal construction——"

"You seem pleased."

"Pleased? I'm delighted! I never thought we could have a real Gothic church again. We've got so many phonies. But this will be unique in America."

"That's nice."

"That's wonderful! No steel—not modern tools—just stone —and men. You know what it'll do for them? And for architecture? Nothing like it since the Middle Ages."

The priest caught fire now. "Yes! Yes! It will be the men's church. And we can teach them things with everything that goes into it."

"You bet! Look—I'll draw you simple plans, just dimensions. Then you teach your men. Get craftsmen in for everything, but make your apprentices learn their trade. Get me? No machine stuff at all."

"It may be pretty awful."

"It won't be. Not when they get the idea."

"No," the priest said, "it won't be. And they will get the idea."

2. In the months that followed Mrs. O'Malley had received only one note from Brendon. It was from Spain. It said:

Dear Mom: This is a funny thing I have done, because I wasn't sure if it was right or not. I did it anyway. Don't think I didn't enjoy the seminary. I did. But it wasn't for me. I got itchy one day and here I am. This is the life! Don't worry about me. I'm a pretty good flier. Write me. Love, Brendon.

3.   Father Hyland had thought at first that it was the spring that had brought the fever, then that it was the strain of summer, but now it was early autumn and he was still burning.

Time—he was praying for time! Letters from the chancery offices he tore open. There were responses, promises, but not enough.

Today as he sat there looking at the bundle of notes the writing was blurred. These were requests from the men, many of them impossible, but he must see them all and explain.

Request: To attend father's funeral. Annotation: This man has been once, while his father was ill. One visit alone allowed. Request refused.

Request: Interview. Allan Green. Note: Granted. Set time. Also arrange to have Green transferred to work in this office. Possible miscarriage of justice.

Request: Marriage case. Once, attempted before J. P. Annotation: Can be fixed up. Write chancery.

Request: Boiler burst in home. Note: Informed man everything fixed. Still unsatisfied. Get report, Catholic Charities, Vincent de Paul.

Request: More books for library. Better subject matter. Note: Get, get, get! Question, where? How?

Request: See Kotas in solitary. See Palmieri in infirmary. See Williams in F. L. Send for . . .

He signed all the notes, appointing times for interviews, and called Bud Horne, giving him instructions for the day. As usual, just about as soon as work started, the guard would announce mess time and march his men off. Then in the afternoon there would be exercise in the Big Yard, time out for coffee, supper. Things might be idle in the rest of the prison. They were not here. And a pile of correspondence would be left for him.

In the meantime he had seen a dozen prisoners, drafted

twenty or thirty letters, called at the infirmary, dashed rapidly over to the State Hospital to find a man who had forgotten that he had sent for him, leave a book or two for Tom Riordan, and come back to the prison in time to say a word to the visitors.

Mrs. Galupi spoke little English, but he gathered that her best son was here, unjustly, because he had always been a good boy at home. Wasn't the blessed padre supposed to help?

Mrs. Dubois said that her husband didn't really steal a car, he just took a ride with a few beers in him. And who was going to take care of the kids now?

Mrs. Dangerford (colored) had no place to spend the night. He would arrange for her.

Then back to the correspondence and the rounds of the cells so that he could find the men who would not come to him—there still were many—and work with them until time for lights out. Then he took his two bags, filled with letters, soiled altar cloths, official memoranda, brochures on counseling which he seldom read, and usually a thermos bottle of coffee which he had intended to drink and which he had forgotten.

He went back to his little cottage to find that after he had eaten a peanut-butter sandwich, stale now after the day, it was eleven o'clock with just time for his Breviary. After that he planned his correspondence, read a little, wished he had had time for the piano, said his rosary, knelt for a moment before the Blessed Sacrament, and after he had weighed himself, went to bed.

He thought it rather amusing. He was losing a pound a day. Like clockwork. Exactly a pound . . .

The alarm went off at six.

4. The early afternoon had been too still.

Cyrus Turner, hiding in the Vermont hills, had thrown the little soap sculpture that he had made into the fireplace. He had forced himself to work on small things, but he knew the feverish desire for something grandiose. His Wagnerian mood, they had called it. That is what he was good for—big things.

He looked at his hands, crushed them together. Now the knots of muscles between thumb and finger had softened. He was all softened. The big gesture had softened the tough fiber of him all over and he was weak, a white slug crawling under these rotten woods.

Then the stillness passed. In the growing strength of the wind he felt better. Like a fierce song the wind sprang that afternoon until the trees around cracked and the roof timbers of his cabin lifted, strained, were sliced off.

He was outside then, and a moment later, almost carried along by the wind he was off toward the village. This was a good wind. This was the first satisfactory big wind ever seen. Destructive. The village is suffering, beaten. The waters of Lake Champlain, beyond, were a blackness, a raging. The rains began.

In the village they did not know who the strange bearded man was. He took charge of things, not wild from the mountains as they had thought, but with cool command. They got out of the railroad shacks when he told them to, before the walls crumpled. He held up a broken ceiling until they saved the baby and then leaped clear. He bedded a group down in the station, another in the post office.

There in the light someone recognized him through beard and all, from the twin pictures of the "Wanted" poster. Cyrus Turner, wanted for strangling. And his hands, gnarled, bitten, bleeding where the wood he had upheld had burned through —they saw his hands. They were afraid.

He was not afraid. This is what he was good for. The big things.

When they came after him through the roaring, beautiful night, with the patrol boat after his stolen motor, the searchlight making spots through the wildness of the hurricane, he was exultant. This pursuit he understood. It leaped to music, great in his ears.

He was not afraid when he jumped ashore near Plattsburg, and he laughed once when he thought he had eluded them, because with this stolen car he could outrace them through fallen trees, for he was not afraid. They were.

It was what he understood. Primitive. No modern method of pursuit, electric light, telephone. Just wreck of hurricane.

Even when they picked up his trail, following through blackness, going west somewhere, road signs down, he exulted. He was made for this. They were not.

So he came to a high place in the road, and branches belted against the windshield, slowing him down, and across, below, he saw great arc lights jutting into the sky and snooping down on something set above mists like a castle of the gods in a last act.

His motor went dead. He stepped on the starter too hard, heard a gurgle, smelled overflowing gas. He looked again. A round tower on the enclosed hill swayed, wind-obliqued, crumpled. The hill castle now was surmounted by nothing but light.

Again he tried to start the car. Headlights just behind through fallen branches. He turned off his own lights and stepped out of the car into the wind. With his great hands he pushed, almost lifted, the car forward to the brow of the hill, helped by hurricane, and then, as it began to roll, he leaped aboard and in pitch blackness let it gain in speed, down a crazy curve, the motor turning over at last so that he could go faster, feel the blare lights behind him slit to pinpricks and finally disappear in racing darkness.

Over him something hung. He could sense the wall. There was a tree down and he veered to avoid it and remembered distinctly afterward, before everything went black, how easily the motor crumpled into his lap, how there was silence except for wind, and how, after they lifted him out, captured, he heard two men talk.

"A tower went down in the prison."

"Only a silo."

"Clears the place for the church."

It meant nothing to him. He was happy from the chase, the night, the wind. This is the way he would have planned his taking. No sniveling. No slugs, white, crushed under the rotten bark. The woods themselves fell about him. He must crash into an invincible wall, be defeated by the prison itself.

Cyrus Turner was captured immediately under the walls of Dannemora, the night of the hurricane, 1938.

5. Father Hyland looked up the hill that bright morning after the hurricane. Yesterday there had been the old silo and the barns; now there was a heap of rubbish. Whether anyone wanted it or not, the demolition had begun. The guards twitted him about how God had begun his job of clearance for the church, taking things into His own hands. He rather thought He had.

With Joe Hogan beside him, he surveyed the work remaining. Even with the help of the hurricane it was immense, for except for its height the hilltop was the least suitable spot in the enclosure; the land was uneven; there was a ledge of rock; down the middle of it stretched the abandoned ruin of wall he had noticed on his first day; and the wild jumble of what had been silo and dairy presented a sorry spectacle.

Joe Hogan said, "The wind knocked down the buildings, Father, but it can't take away the barnyard. It's a funny place for a church."

"I don't think so, Joe. I think it's good."

"How do you figure that?"

"The stable. It's significant. Christ was born in a stable."

Joe Hogan surveyed the ruins and the offal. "If you can see that, you're good." Then he stopped, sobered. The priest did see more than most men saw. Who'd ever think of that one, now? "And how about the wall? You got that figured out?"

"Yes," Father Hyland said. "I know what that means too."

He said no more, but went on measuring spaces for the foundation all that morning until he and the guard were ready to stake off the place that should be set aside for the foundation. At the end of the day, with the little pegs in place and the neat cords strung, Father Hyland said, "There's our church. I wish you could work on it with me."

"Maybe I can."

"How? You know how much influence I have around here. I can't even get prisoners moved, let alone guards."

"Oh, I don't know. You do pretty well in the long run. Why don't you think up a fancy title for me—like chief engineer?"

"Are you one?"

"I had a course."

"That's better than I can say for my other engineers."

"Me and a gang of hoodlums. What do we know about building a church?"

"What does any of us know?"

"O.K. When do we start?"

"Tomorrow."

"I'll fix it up with the principal keeper. I'll be with you tomorrow."

The next day the work began, and with Joe Hogan as chief engineer it continued. Obviously, once the barns had collapsed, men had to be assigned to the work of removing them and new dairies had to be built beyond the limits of the church enclosure. Almost of necessity preparations for the church were begun.

The days that followed ran together in the priest's mind. In prison overalls he carried rocks, sorted beams that could be salvaged from the barns, uprooted stumps and stones, cajoled the men into working with him. He tried to show them, first by his own labors, then by his words, what this work meant, but they were unresponsive, doing as little as they could. Inevitably, however, the space for the church was cleared and he was ready to dig. He took up a shovel one day and began.

"Hey, Padre," Hogan called over to him, "you can't dig the whole cellar yourself!"

"What else can I do? It's got to be done."

"Then why don't you look down the hill?"

Winding up from the East Gate came a parade of bulldozers, trench-cutters, steam shovels. The priest stared in amazement.

"I prayed," he said, "but I didn't pray for that much."

He was ready to enjoy his moment when Bud Horne, at his elbow, said, "There's a man calling for you at the infirmary."

"All right. I'll go down."

He went at once, glancing only a couple of times at the machines that were now halfway up the long hill.

The man who was calling for him was a member of the band, and of the type that sometimes he thought of as a slug: he recognized the dry scalp, the preternatural pallor, and the nervous eyes of the drug addict. But there was something else beyond the craving. There was fear.

"We had a fight over a band instrument——"

So Father Hyland knew. "Yes," he said.

"I never done a dirty thing in my life. I was a hophead. I filed down a flute and I stuck it into his belly. All night I hear him cursing me. I needed the white stuff."

"Thank God," the priest murmured.

"What did you say? Aw—you wouldn't understand."

How could Father Hyland explain the relief he felt, learning, after all these months, that the killing of the musician had not been pointless, trivial—that even if the reason lay in drug craving, there was some reason. He knew now that intervening months had not cured him of the initial horror.

"I understand more than you do," he said at last.

"That's good."

"I was with—your friend—when he died."

"Did he curse me out?"

"No. He said he shouldn't have fought over the tuba. He told me to tell you that."

The musician's fists clenched. "He squealed on me. He told you——"

"No, he didn't. He said sometime you might come to me—*someone* might come—the way you did today. And if they did, he said that was his message—he didn't blame you. Only I never thought you'd come—after all this time."

"I get it. He was a good Joe. And look—can you get me——"

"No. I know what you're going to ask. You want me to get the doctors to give you a shot in the arm. I won't. They'll do it if you need it."

"Naw—they won't—that's the trouble—and he comes after me!"

"He won't come after you any more."

"How do you know?"

"Because you're not afraid any more. He never came after you. You were after yourself—it was all inside you. Now that's gone. And we're going to wipe the last of it out as soon as you go to confession."

After the confession the priest had every intention of hurrying back to the hilltop, and he could not understand why he had to stop so often. He was happy—happier than he had ever been. This was his first real success with any man in prison, and if the penitent had had a nightmare taken away from him, the confessor, too, had had a horror lifted, which had weighed on him more than he realized. But still he had to stop so often to get his breath.

When at last he reached the cleared space at the top of the hill he found Hogan with a long face. The machinery had halted on East Hill.

"What's the matter?"

"I should have known. It's not for us. That's the machinery for the new dairy, see?"

"Oh."

"It's a merry-go-round. Those things cost two hundred and fifty grand. Get the idea?"

"I get it." All that money for a dairy—for pedigreed cows—nothing for the church. But today there had been one soul at peace with himself and God, and nobody could take that away.

The priest began to dig again. Then he stopped, not from pain this time but because he had had a sudden thought. The other day he had realized that he had no rights, nothing he could command, and he had been disturbed because he had had to be a beggar. But why not? Francis of Assisi had been a beggar. Who had ever assessed or evaluated his contribution to life? All the great mendicant orders of the Church were official beggars. Why not he? If God wanted it this way——

He put down his shovel.

"Where are you going?" Hogan shouted after him.

"I'm going a-begging."

He crossed over, through the wire gate, to the east mountain, and found the foreman.

"I've come begging," he said. "I want the use of your steam shovel when you're not using it. My men can run it—I think. I have a chief engineer. We want to dig a cellar for a church."

He got the loan of the steam shovel and somehow, working at odd hours, ultimately dug the foundation.

Then he and Joe Hogan stood there. Looking down into the pit, they could see water seeping in, a great black pool filling up.

"Faust, Zweite Theil," the priest said.

"What?"

"Goethe—a play. *Faust.* He had been on top of a mountain—a cursed mountain—Walpurgisnacht with demons—and at last he dug a grave, his own grave, like this. A great black grave."

CHAPTER EIGHT

When Joe Hogan tried to tell Mrs. Hyland what had happened, he found it difficult. He did not want to alarm her, and yet she should be prepared if the worst came to the worst.

"We were just standing there talking," Hogan said. "Then he began to say some awful things, kind of in a foreign language. There was something wrong and he was too near the edge of the excavation. I put my arm around his shoulder, and it's a good thing I did, because he sort of clutched himself as if he had been stabbed, and then he slumped down. He might have fallen in."

"I'm glad you were there, Mr. Hogan," Mrs. Hyland said. "You're one of the guards he spoke about."

"The only one spoke to him much at first," Hogan thought, but he went on. "Then we got a stretcher for him and took him down to the infirmary. He came to then."

"What did the doctors say?"

"He's pretty sick, ma'am."

"I know that. He's been starving himself. I should have stayed with him."

"You couldn't have helped."

"I could have fed him."

"It wouldn't have done any good. He *is* starving, but not for that reason. They say he has a complete stoppage of the stomach."

"It's pretty serious?"

"Yes. I won't kid you. That's why they rushed him to Montreal." He could not tell her that the doctors had said he had only a 40-per-cent chance of recovery. They told him to clean up any business that he had.

"I would have gone with him if you'd told me."

"There wasn't time. It had to be quick. He has the best physicians."

"Who?"

"Sir John Hingston—Dr. Hoen. They don't come any better."

"That's good. When is the operation?"

"It's—about now."

"I ought to be there. I couldn't be with my eldest boy when he died in the war in France. The night we got word we told Ambrose. He was in the high-school play, and he went right on. Good too. Then, afterward, when he graduated, he was too young for service and he wanted to do something, so he worked all year on a farm. Thought it kind of helped—doing something in his brother's place. Brother was killed in the war. I couldn't be there."

"Father Ambrose isn't going to die, Mrs. Hyland."

"No. He never gives up. He went on to college, and he hated it as first. Then he went to Catholic University and he loved that. He never stopped. Nothing ever stopped him. When did you say the operation was?"

"About now."

"He won't stop. Once in the seminary he almost stopped. He didn't. He met a girl at Trinity—Kitty Scanlon that was—and she said to him, 'I'm going to be a Carmelite, and you're going back and be a priest.' She's Mother Angela. And he's a priest. He'll come through."

"I know he will."

"He's got work to do. He's got to finish a church."

She knew.

2.   The case of the State vs. Cyrus Turner was conducted in a small courthouse in upper New York. It was a false Dutch building set in a town square, and to it each morning the crowd came. The trial had attracted a great deal of attention. Turner was well known.

At nine the chatter would stop, the judge enter, seat himself, and prepare to be bored until recess. The district attorney would thunder, the defense counsel would speak quietly and drip vitriol. He had taken a line from the Halls-Mills case which had so many witnesses, and from the Elwell case which had so many confessions, and had introduced all kinds of professional testimony so that it became successively clear that:

The victim had died of strangulation.

Death had been caused by cerebral thrombosis.

Actual cause of demise had been gun wounds in the abdomen.

Death was accidental, due to the shock of attack.

Probable cause of death had been choking on some hard object.

The defense did not claim that Ralph had died of a combination of these causes, but of each separately. And from moment to moment the jury was convinced that Cyrus Turner had killed or had not killed Ralph, depending on the current professional testimony.

It was confusion. The case dragged on and on. The newspaper people were enchanted.

Fannie Hurst was there.

3.   In Montreal they were wheeling Father Ambrose Hyland into the operating room. He was saying, "Look, God, if all You

want is a hole in the ground, that's all right with me. But if You want a church—it's up to You."

"It's up to You . . ."

4. Carlos Santa Cruz was hard pressed for it. He had never worried about money before but now he wanted something for Mona for Christmas. She had posed so beautifully. And she was so expensive. And worried all the time. She had been reading about the Turner trial and Carlos knew that she had been in love with Turner, still was, perhaps. Certainly she was not in love with Carlos.

As for himself, how could he tell? Perhaps this was the only way he could ever be in love with anyone, not having them in love with him. He wondered sometimes how people ever got married. Two people never fell in love with each other, always with someone else.

He did not want to buy her affection. He could not. Always she was cruel to him. But it pleased him to give her presents, to pay her handsomely for posing. It was his happiness. So he needed money.

Before, he had eked out whatever was necessary for his own needs by doing that engraving work for other people, not caring, really, whether Ruffino paid him or not. As yet he had never manufactured a bad bill, merely doing the engraving for others, and that was comparatively safe, but now he needed money.

Carlos Santa Cruz spent most of the mornings painting and repainting Mona as the Madonna. The rest of the day and half the night he worked at making perfect twenty-dollar bills. He almost had it.

Christmas was coming.

5. It seemed to Father Hyland, climbing back into consciousness after the operation, that he was emerging out of a black pit into which he had fallen. And then he remembered the last clear moment, standing beside the excavation and talking about

his grave. There had been a strong arm around him that had pulled him back.

"It wasn't time to die," he said.

Dr. Hingston was bending over him. "You didn't want to. That's what saved you."

"Not only that. Something else."

"We gave you up once."

"Saint Dismas didn't. I've got work to do."

"Yes. After a while. You've got a long rest coming to you."

"What's the date?"

"December eighth."

"I've got to be back for Christmas."

"I don't think you can quite make that."

"I've got to. The men want me." He stopped and scowled thoughtfully. "No. They don't want me. But they need me. If they wanted me, I wouldn't care so much."

"Don't talk now."

He did not talk, but he could think. Perhaps if my men cared about me I couldn't be so sure. Then I might go back to them because they wanted me and I wanted their admiration and respect. This is better. Now I know there is nothing for myself. Last Christmas—nearly Christmas now—not one word of gratitude—and none this Christmas—any Christmas. Only for Christ this work, in Christ and through Him. Nothing for self.

It came to him then that his whole heart, his whole life lay with his antagonistic flock. In that at least, however poorly, he could imitate Christ's love—always God was the rejected suitor, never having His great love returned.

6. The case of the State vs. Cyrus Turner closed that morning. The counsel for the defense had not achieved quite as much as he had hoped for, which was, of course, complete exoneration, but at least the sentence had been lighter than anyone had expected.

Cyrus Turner would not die. There were more years yet.

His sentence would begin just before Christmas, at Clinton Prison, Dannemora.

7. At Christmas, over the doctor's protest, Father Hyland went back to Dannemora. He was not able to walk yet, but he managed it slowly, going in the gate, feeling the Siberian cold, being met at the door of the auditorium by the familiar and finally welcome blast of steam, odor of people, smells of dinner, laundry hanging out to dry, and the sounds from below.

He was a little late for Mass. The elderly priest whom the bishop had sent to help out for Christmas was already turning around to read the Gospel. The old priest stopped and looked at Ambrose standing there in the rear of the hall. The eyes of the congregation turned in his direction, and his men saw him.

Then even the rattle of dishes from below seemed to cease, and there was a silence. He turned to shrink unobtrusively into the back benches, but they were filled.

Silently four men stood up. He thought they were making room for him and he was grateful. But they were not. They lifted him up on their shoulders, reverently carried him down the aisle, brought him up the steps to the chancel, and enthroned him in the one good chair.

The old priest read the Gospel. It was Christmas.

He was home.

BOOK TWO: SPIRE OVER THE WALL

CHAPTER ONE

When in late January he was able to get to his office again, he asked Joe Hogan how it had happened.

"The men," he said. "They're different. When did they change?"

"It was gradual," Hogan said. "I could see it coming. I don't think you could. You were too close to them. But I'll tell you about the real change. I can time that to the minute."

"You can?"

"Yes. I'd been up to break the news to your mother. It was the day of your operation. I knew the time, but I didn't have it down to seconds. When was it, actually?"

"A little before noon. About eleven-thirty—or just before."

"Yes. That's right. That's when they figured it."

"How did they know?"

"Search me. How do they know anything? But anyhow, I had just got back and I dropped in at the factory. I didn't think the men knew you very well there. I remember it was noisy as usual, and I had to shout some orders I was supposed to give. It was quarter past eleven. They had fifteen minutes before they shut down for chow. I remember that because I had hurried back from Chateaugay to catch them while they were still working. I remember the noise too."

"It's always noisy there."

"Yes. Then you can imagine what a sudden quiet would be. At eleven-twenty everything stopped—machines, yells, talk, everything."

"That's funny."

"That's what I thought. I was sure it was a strike or the beginning of a riot. I grabbed my truncheon, ready for anything. I didn't shout at them, thank God, because the other guards were not doing anything either, just standing there still."

"I don't get it."

"Don't you? Where were you at eleven-twenty?"

"I was—I was well under ether. They were—— Oh. Yes."

"Yes. All through the prison there was that silence. It lasted only a minute. Padre, I don't know whether all those men were praying for you or not, but I do know what that silence meant. And when it was broken, I heard one dark boy say, 'O Lord, let him be!' "

"Lee Sapis Robinson."

For a moment the two men did not speak. The familiar sound of the typewriters from the library came to them. Then Father Hyland asked, "How do you make it out? What came over them?"

"I've got it figured out, I think. You see, the men in here, first of all, they're always being bossed and cared for and looked after. Did you ever think what his canary means to Bud Horne? It's something he can boss and care for and look after. That was the first thing. When you were a big shot, changing everything, as far as they could see, getting everything you wanted, pals with the warden—see how they felt? Then you broke. They could do something for you. Get it?"

"I think so."

"Now you're theirs. They're going to take care of you. You watch."

"How about the second thing?"

"Caste system. Most of them are sheep, and they follow along. We know who the leaders are and we keep our eyes on them. Never mind the others. So, I guess, one of the leaders said you were a good Joe."

"Who was he? Do you know?"

"I think so. He isn't a very nice man, Padre. I wouldn't like him for an enemy."

"How about as a friend?"

"That's different. I could put up with that."

"I wonder if I know."

Father Hyland smiled as he picked up a tab from the top of the pile on his desk, a request for an interview, and pushed it over to Hogan.

"Could be," the guard said. He had read the name.

"But I can't remember anything I ever did for him."

"Maybe you didn't. Maybe that's the secret of it."

The priest struck the desk with the palm of his hand. "That's it! I've got it!"

"Got what? Catch a fly?"

"No! No! The whole secret. Look. These men are terribly indebted, aren't they? Haven't anything of their own any more, can't do anything. That's why they seemed to be ungrateful—like all underprivileged people who haven't got enough. Not even their own self-respect. So they take, grasp, demand, because they can't give. And they get tired saying thank you. I've got it!"

"Take it easy."

"You know what I'm going to do? I'm going to ask them for more and more—put terrific demands on them—make them conscious of what they can do."

"That's something!"

"That's what the building of the church will mean. I started out with the idea of helping them. But now that's all changed. They're going to build a church—for God. Even for me, if necessary, if I can't get any higher motive into them. They're going to give!"

"You've got something there."

"I'm going to get myself so terribly indebted to them that anything I do for them won't half repay them. And they're going to know it. That's it. That's the answer."

"That's part of it. Of course you'll have to give them something."

"Oh, I will. But they'll be little things, just by way of thank you. And the big things will be big thank yous. That's all."

"Like Christmas?"

"What about Christmas?"

"Like the things you gave them for Christmas."

"Oh. Last Christmas. That's what bothers me—that I couldn't send them anything at all this Christmas."

Joe Hogan beamed. "That isn't the way I heard it." He rose to go. "Oh, Lord," Father Hyland was saying, "I wish we could begin on that church now!"

"Thank God you can't." Hogan looked out the window at the three feet of snow. "Take care of yourself, Padre."

When Joe Hogan was gone, Father Hyland went into the outer office.

"Men," he said, "I know I've worked you pretty hard and I don't know if I've said thanks. But you see I've got to ask you for still more. I can't do as much as I did and you fellows have got to take over."

Dominic beamed. "Sure, Padre. Anything."

"All right. See this mail here? It piles up. I think I could get the principal keeper to let you take some of it to your cells at night. You could clean up a lot that way. Of course it'll cut down your free time, but I don't see any other way, if you're going to build a church this spring."

"What's holding us up?" Cassidy asked.

"Weather for one thing. Me for another—and money. We can't even start laying concrete for the cellar until we have enough in the bank. The bishop won't give permission. That's why we need those letters to go out."

"We'll get them out." Dominic was enthusiastic.

Bud Horne looked over his spectacles. He disapproved of exuberance.

"We can cut down a lot of waste motion," he said.

"Can we? Good. How, Bud?"

"I have a plan. May I show it to you? In your office?"

"Certainly."

A chill had been cast. The priest could feel the glacier quality in the atmosphere, but he was determined to be receptive. Yet the warmth had gone out of Dominic and Cassidy. Even Bill Martin, who had said nothing, seemed to sense it.

"Come on in," the priest said.

For days Bud Horne had been working, foreseeing this

change, anticipating the day. He was always ready. Now he had prepared a draft of a plan for fund raising. Every detail was carefully looked into. There were lists of prospects, neatly tabulated, according to their resources, businesses, possible lines of interest.

"That's the sucker list," he said.

"Oh. Oh yes." The priest did not smile. He had thought of these people as benefactors.

"And see this."

Again, with the utmost care, the various projects were broken down and budgeted—Christmas Fund, Church Building Plan, Welfare Program, Petty-cash Charities, Donations (General), and Overhead. All very clear and all very, very cold, and all, perhaps, a little overambitious.

But, without being asked, Bud Horne had worked on this every night in his cell in the time that he would have otherwise spent on his case. Already the plan filled four large copybooks. Carefully, too, he had kept a record of every moment employed on the project. Hours and minutes were tabulated on carefully ruled sheets. Bud Horne knew exactly how much overtime he had spent on the campaign for the Church of the Good Thief.

When Father Hyland had gone, rather carefully, through the whole proposition, he was disturbed. It was all very neat and efficient—too efficient, he feared, and far too ambitious. But worse than that, it had reduced charity to a matter of business. He could never use such a plan. It defeated everything he stood for. Yet what could he say? Bud Horne had worked hard on this.

"There's a lot of thought in this, Bud," he said. "A lot of work. You beat me to it." But it was all useless. How could he tell him? Perhaps he did not need to.

"Here's another angle—Publicity. Have you thought of that?"

What else had he thought about in the lectures he had planned, the people he had seen?

"Maybe not enough, Bud."

"Then pipe this. It's good stuff."

Bud had a folder of clippings, all written by Dempster Mac-Murphy of Chicago. They were about Dismas, the Good Thief. Father Hyland was tempted to read them then, but he put them aside until later.

"That's what we need, Chaplain. Stuff like that. It's full of malarkey but it gets them. 'Shoestring catches of souls.' That's what he says Dismas makes. See? I could think up things like that and you could say them. 'There's no such thing as a condemned man!'"

"Father Flanagan of Boys Town said something like that."

"It's still good, isn't it?"

"Yes."

"How about this—'Be Pro-con.' That's a good motto."

I said that myself once, Father Hyland thought. I'm glad he approves of it. "Yes. That's all right."

"Or, 'Thieves Steal Heaven.'"

"Mm, hmm."

"I'll write them all out. I'll give them to you," Bud Horne said.

"Thanks. That'll be fine, Bud. You do that."

His secretary went out then, satisfied, leaving Father Hyland free for his first interview—with Lucky Luciano.

The meeting was brief, but it was quite clear. Lucky had heard that the padre might be going to New York. While there he might as well pick up thirty thousand dollars for his new church.

"I never was against churches," Lucky said. "I believe in them. I think they do good."

"So do I."

"So I want to help. You could use thirty grand, couldn't you?"

"I certainly could."

"I thought so. And the deal is on the level."

"If it's for a church, I suppose it might just as well be."

"Sure. That's what I figured. Nothing phony about this. All you need is to lay down a grand."

"I don't think I have it to lay down."

"No? Don't worry. I'll see you get that too."

"What will I lay it down on?"

"It's the numbers racket, see? The thing's fixed. You can't lose."

"And it's perfectly straight? Absolutely on the level? I don't get it."

"Sure. They're always fixed, aren't they? Somebody's going to win. We got to have a winner. You might as well be it. Get it?"

"I'm sorry, Lucky—I——"

"Look. You could go to the governor with the kale in your hand. You'd say, 'See, Lehman? I don't need your money. I got my own!' What could Lehman say to that?"

"Nothing, I suppose. Only it isn't the governor any more. He's given permission."

"That right? Then who's holding up the works?"

"The bishop."

"Same idea. Wave the dough at him."

"Lucky, you don't do that with bishops. He might ask where it came from."

"Suppose he did! Didn't he ever run a bingo? What's the idea?"

"I'm just afraid I can't do it. I know it's a hot tip, but you see how it is, don't you?"

Lucky shook his head. He did not see how it was. He kept shaking his head wonderingly and, ever after adopted the patronizing attitude that one might take toward a well-meaning child who was not quite bright.

Father Hyland did not allow himself so much as a smile until Lucky was well out of the office, but then he could scarcely wait to get to his cottage and tell his mother about the incident.

Mrs. Hyland was staying with him for these few days until, as she said, he was well enough to shift for himself. While she was serving the dinner, jumping up every few minutes to get some more, he told her about Lucky. He could hear her laughing from the kitchen.

"I wish you'd let him help you," she said, coming in with the deep-dish apple pie. "I'd bet on it."

"Mother," he said solemnly, "you're immoral."

"That's what comes of having a son a thief. Wait till I get some cheese. Traveling around in bad company."

"I know the nicest murderers now."

"How's the coffee? Oh, wait. You're not supposed to have that. I'll get your tea. I do think most murderers are well-intentioned."

"Want somebody bumped off? I *could* see Lucky again."

"Nobody but that butcher. His beef is tough. I'll do the dishes later."

Mrs. Hyland sat down at last. She was not afraid any more that Ambrose would overdo it because, as the winter had worn on, she had discovered a new buoyancy in him which meant that everything was going well. When he felt like that, nothing could stop him. But he mustn't get too cock-sure, either.

"Ambrose," she said, "I guess you're getting plenty of contributions, aren't you? But don't you think for a minute it's going to stay this way. A lot is due to Dempster MacMurphy. I don't want to be a Jonah, but when people stop being excited about that hoodlum saint of his, your contributions are bound to fall off."

"My," he said, "you're well read! Bud Horne just gave me a sheaf of material by MacMurphy. It looks good." He lit the black cigar he enjoyed after one of his mother's dinners. "But don't you go around thinking things are too promising right now."

"You wouldn't look so self-satisfied if they weren't."

"It isn't that. Just somehow—I know we're going to win."

"So do I. But what are you counting on?"

"We're going to put on a really big drive. I can't rely on the bishops for everything so I'm going to New York to see Joe Madden. Somebody got him interested in Saint Dismas and Joe will have ideas."

"I suppose you're relying on Saint Dismas too?" she asked.

"Of course. He's the patron of thieves."

"Including yourself," she added. "But you know there's one thing you should rely on more. You don't think half enough about Mother Angela and her Carmelites. Bet you haven't answered her letter."

"Bet I have," he said triumphantly. "I got another letter from her. She says she's going to send me something."

"What?"

"She wouldn't tell."

"Hmmph. Women's secrets. I bet it's prayers. I've heard you preaching about the power of prayers so much you've got me believing in it. Now with those nuns—there's prayers for you."

"Yes," he said. "There is. And there're other prayers going on in the prison that you wouldn't believe."

He did not intend to detract from the efficacy of the Carmelites in their cloister, but somehow he began to talk about Max Bergner and Tom Riordan and the possibility of a life of penance and of true mysticism within the walls. Everything now seemed to center on the prison. All his thoughts were there.

"You think about them all the time, don't you?"

"Most of the time."

"That's good. And it's new. You didn't used to feel that way. I'm glad."

He had not told even her about last Christmas. It had been embarrassing enough to have been carried on the men's shoulders, yet it had made all the difference in the world. But he could tell her another incident which capped the story about Lucky Luciano and had the same point. She would understand.

A delegation had come in. The spokesman, lean-jawed, a scar across his temple, third finger of his left hand missing, had said, "Padre, we hear you're going to need money. We got a proposition."

"Good." Father Hyland opened a fresh box of cigars. "Let's hear it."

"We're all from Philly. We know that joint. You see that we get out of here two-three days. That's all we need. You can work it easy—the old lady sick or something. Just four of us. Then don't ask no questions. Savvy?"

"Yes," he had said, "I savvy. How much can you get me?"

"How much you want?"

"About fifty thousand to start with."

"Fifty grand! Hey, what you think we are?"

"I didn't think you were pikers."

"Pikers? Who? Us? Say—you make it a week; we'll get the dough for you, or just two nights, two guns."

"No can do." He wondered if this were the time to preach to them about fundamental honesty and decided that it wasn't. They were offering him the only service they could. Doubtless their Robin Hood code made them feel justified.

"I'm sorry," he added. "Can't you see why I couldn't get you out for that?"

"Yeah," one of them said. "Yeah. We thought of that. We thought maybe you'd think it was a racket—us wanting out. But it isn't, Padre. It's on the level."

"That's straight," a third one put in—red hair, small mole on left cheek, thyroid eyes—"even if you can't spring us, just get a kite out to the rest of the gang in Philly for us and they'll come through."

There was so much eagerness, so much earnestness in their offer that it was a shame to laugh, but he could not help it then any more than he could now, telling about it to his mother.

"Didn't you even say it was wrong to steal?" she asked him.

"I did worse than that. I laughed at them," he replied. "They got the idea. And when they had gone all my cigars were gone too. You see, it's pretty useless trying to give them the idea of a straight moral code. They invent their own."

"And that's all wrong," his mother said.

"What is?"

"Your own moral code. It won't work."

"Why won't it?"

"Why, Ambrose," she said, "you know that. It's like the multiplication table. If you use the wrong one, you get the wrong answer. You can't make up one for yourself. That's what I think about morality."

"Say!" he said. "I take that all back about your being immoral! Who taught you your theology anyway?"

"Common sense," she said.

2.   Lee Sapis Robinson had no visitors. He never would have any, because he just didn't know anybody on the outside. He watched Greeney leaving the gallery, and he was not envious. Some boys were always eating themselves out because others got the breaks. He couldn't see that it hurt him any, if Greeney had visitors.

There wasn't anything he had to worry about now that he had found his way out. This was the best thing he could do. They kept telling him he was useless, didn't they, and he guessed he was. So he could wait until dark again and break off a little more bedspring into the rag of sock. He wasn't near ready yet. Someday he would be. His finger muscles were growing powerful strong.

He had his own way.

Going to the visitors' gallery, Greeney was smiling because he was sure it would be his wife. Millie would bring the baby he had never seen and she would promise to help him. The only reason she hadn't come before was that at first she had been sore at him for getting messed up. Then she was going to have the baby, and women feel different then. After she'd had it, of course, she would have been all right.

Suddenly a wave of feeling which he could not understand swept through him. He stopped, almost breaking the line, and the guard spoke sharply. Greeney didn't know what it was that he felt, but this was his first visitor, and all of a sudden he had seen himself there behind the plate-glass window and both of them trying to talk. He supposed it was shame, but it didn't feel the way it had when he felt ashamed. It was plain fright.

You didn't show that. You walked right ahead and you

cracked wise about the wife and the glass between you. You didn't let the men around you know how bad you felt, because if you did, they might feel that way too.

It was part of the code he was learning. This and what he had learned before—that it was wrong to say you were guilty. That was part of the law too. You didn't do that, because if you did the other guys would crack up maybe, and you'd have a lot of confessions. That wouldn't be good.

So he went on, chin up. Each time the line paused at a locked gate he was glad, because he thought his legs wouldn't carry him any farther.

Now he knew. He didn't want to see anybody. He wanted to stay inside here, deep back beyond bars, safe from outside. You couldn't tell what you'd hear, could you? Inside, they were all the same, but outside people thought different. They'd be talking about you. You'd hear the things they said. People you trusted let you down. As long as you didn't know—as long as you could let one day go along after another, still fighting, but fighting with your own kind. He looked around. These men in here were his own kind. Outside, people were against them. They thought different from cons.

Greeney didn't want to see his Millie. He was relieved when she was not there. The visitor was his brother. He could give him the brushoff and he did, because he didn't want to hear anything and he couldn't have given the brushoff to Millie. Only one thing came to him through what his brother said, and it made him feel good. Funny it made him feel good.

Millie was running around. She had had the baby and she was talking divorce now.

He didn't know why he should be glad of that, but he was. It set him inside and her outside, and they'd never be together again anyway. She had her own ideas. She was giving him the gate. She thought she was right. Only she was wrong as hell. They wouldn't do that in here. They were all better than she was. In here, anyhow, they were honest. Outside everybody was crooked.

Outside they hadn't been caught yet.

There was no gradual pulling up out of darkness for Brendon O'Malley. One moment he could not remember, and the next was all brightness. He was lying in a small patio under the most brilliant of Spanish skies—a violence of blue over him. His arm, bent across his body, was in a sling. His left leg had a cast to the hip. He knew, without feeling it, that his beard had grown an inch of red.

So it must be a long time that he had been here asleep. He could not remember spinning in. Nothing he could recall. He had been in the ready-room joking with the boys and trying out his new Spanish on them. There had been a lizard on the wall when he closed his eyes and it was not there now that he opened them. That was how he knew that he had slept. A woman's voice said in Spanish, "You look better." The Spanish had a peculiar accent that he could not place.

"I am better," he said.

"Good. If you are hungry I will feed you."

"Thanks," he replied, "but I can feed myself."

The woman laughed musically. "It would be impossible, Brendon."

She knew his name. He must have talked to her.

"How much do you know about me, señorita?"

"Señorita?" She looked oddly at him. "You know my name —and you know that it is also señora. What has happened to you?"

Ironical, he thought, that she should ask him. How did he know? But she was going on. "About you—I know what you told me. Is there more?"

"No. Nothing more. Only I wish you'd tell me again how I got here."

"There is little. We found you on the mountain. There was not much left of your companions. You know that. But today you are changed, little minister."

"How am I different now?"

She patted his cheek. "You have not made love to me in almost five minutes."

Was he in love with her? He saw her dark beauty, a little

too heavy for his tastes. Perhaps he had made love to her. It had been the vogue to make love to every pretty woman, and the recollection of it made him ill. That had been part of the code.

"I'm sorry," he said, "but I don't think I love you."

"Oh, I knew that." She smiled. "It meant nothing. This is a relief."

"I'm glad," he said.

There was a long silence.

"Tell me," he asked, "when I'll be fit to fight again?"

"Now that it is over—who cares?"

"What's over?"

A comprehension came to her. "Brendon," she said, "the war is over. Generalissimo Franco is victorious. The communists are routed." She said it flatly, without rancor or exultation, fingering the crucifix that she wore about her neck. Yet she had called them communists, not loyalists, so she must be of the enemy.

"Are you glad?" he asked, and saw that she looked frightened. "I do not understand you. I don't know what side you're on. I think you're a rebel. But you don't seem glad that the Generalissimo has won."

"Glad?" she asked. "I spit upon him. I would drive daggers into the skin of his flesh."

"But you are a Catholic, aren't you?"

"What else would I be? That is part of my hatred for Generalissimo. How can you forget that—I am a Basque!"

She turned from him and fled, as if she could say no more, but her warm perfume remained clinging in the air. Brendon wanted to shout after her but he could not.

Everything was in a confusion. This Basque woman, a Catholic, hated Franco. He had thought the Romans were all rebels. Why couldn't something stay straight? He had thought that he had awakened to a clear world, black and white, comprehensible—and his first questionings had resulted in a worse confusion.

What was it all about?

He himself—the world all around—needed something sure, some clear code to follow.

But where was it? Where?

Where was the knowledge of good and evil?

3. "What do you need, Padre?" Joe Madden called out from behind the bar as soon as he saw Father Hyland. "You wouldn't be here if you didn't need something!"

The priest said the first thing that came to mind. "Cement," he said.

"Cement?" Joe put his hearing aid in place, which meant that he was going to make a speech. "Hey, you boys!" He darted out through the little trapdoor beneath the bar as if he were going into the ring. "Listen to me, you lugs! Anybody got any cement on him? The padre's from Dannemora. You know that place. You all been reading about it in that Demp-ster MacMurphy fellow. Saint Dismas. That's the guy. He calls him the 'Hoodlum Saint.' That's the saint for dopes like youse."

The restaurant was crowded as usual, and Joe bustled his way to the rear. "Hey, you," he called finally. "You Walsh, there! You're full of cement. What you didn't dump into the East River when you gypped City Hall on the subways. Fork up!"

"Wait a minute," Father Hyland called. "I'd better not have it yet, until the bishop says I can go ahead. Don't rush things!"

Joe Madden had taken the hearing aid out of his ear. "Can't hear a word you're saying, Father." He put the plug back in. "Walsh! How soon can you get the cement up there? Don't go looking at my pretty pictures. You heard me. And say—Corbetta, you're a contractor. Both you boys put the bite on Collins. Lehigh Cement, that is. Get it? Two carloads be enough, Father? Yeah. He says yeah. I'll give you a week to get it there or I'll shut down on your liquor."

Dusting off his hands, Joe Madden came back. "Well, that's settled," he said. "Now what else? What's the promotion?"

Father Hyland outlined the project he had in mind. His

plan was not so elaborate as Bud Horne's had been, but it had in it certain elements of charity.

While he was talking, he noticed two men and a woman with Mr. Dick Ryan. He had heard their names, but he had been in the middle of a story about Bud Horne and his canary, and he knew only that they were Charlie McCabe and Mr. and Mrs. Fitzgerald. When he got to the anecdote of Lucky Luciano and the hot tip on the numbers racket, they roared appreciatively, and he warmed to his subject.

He told them everything, all his dreams, about how this would be a truly medieval project with every bit of the church built by the men themselves, from stones and timbers at hand, foundations and towers and spires rising up on that mountain in a monument of praise where once the sagging barns had stood. He told them how he planned to teach the men, not only the trades, but the greater things—what they had which they could give.

It was wonderful to have such an audience. Joe Madden even kept his hearing aid in, missing nothing. When the priest paused at last, Joe said, "Say. What we need is a model of the church. I'll stick it in the window."

It might be incongruous, the priest thought, in a place like this. Yet would it be? No more incongruous than the church itself within a prison.

"Sure," he said. "We'll do that."

"Swell. Now you hens and hawks get busy." Joe directed his guests, and as Mr. and Mrs. Fitzgerald and Charlie McCabe went back to their own table, Father Hyland asked who they were.

"Don't you read? McCabe—columnist. Swell fellow. And if you haven't got a radio, I'll send you one. Them's *the* Fitzgeralds—radio."

"Good Lord! You mean they'll use all that stuff!"

"They better!"

"I guess I ought to hurry up and see the bishop—fast as I can."

"Sure. Tell him I sent you. Say they're friends of Dick Ryan."

"Say—you're all right. I never knew before how many wonderful people there are in the world."

"Sure are. And by the way, how's Lucky anyhow? Treating you all right, like you said?"

"Very much so. Almost too much so."

"That's good. He's a pal of mine."

"What? Oh yes." He would not pursue this subject. "And Joe—why are you so interested in my lads?"

"Aw, nothing. I was seven years in a boys' home. That's all. I know a lot of thugs never had a chance, like me. Like you said, you got to have something. You got to do something for other people to make you feel right. That's all."

"And you got to make them do things too—like you do, Joe."

"Sure. That's part of the system. They like that swell. Look at Walsh now. Look at him, will you? And say—how did the guys like this Christmas?"

"It was wonderful, Joe. I couldn't help them, but somebody sent them all presents. . . . Say, was that you?"

"Don't know anything about it. They came in your name, didn't they?"

"Yes. But——"

"All I know is—they took up a two-ton truck. So mind your business and shut your trap, and hurry up to the bishop, because there's more trucks where that one comes from. Go up there and convince him."

And the bishop was easy to convince. It was easy to convince the bishop of anything at all these days. He knew that he would never have an auxiliary, and that he would never be replaced.

It was that month, having given his final blessing to the work of the Church of Saint Dismas to be erected from the timbers of an old barn and the hand-hewn stones of an ancient wall, and the cement that had already arrived, that the old Bishop of Ogdensburg died.

CHAPTER TWO

The priest stood on the great outcropping shelf of rock. Beneath him the late snows edged the excavation, and around it stood two hundred of the worst criminals in America, armed with picks and shovels and the instruments of demolition. From the turrets the machine guns were turned upon them; the blue coats of guards mottled the mob of gray. "There'll be trouble, Padre," the guard said, "Too many tools. You're heading for God knows what. They've sent you the worst gang in the prison. Yes, sir. There'll be trouble."

And the priest looked at his men and smiled. He said, "Do you think so?" For though they were lined and marred, their faces were turned up to him, and seeing only their eyes, he was not afraid. Now also he could see back beyond them, to the century of felons who had dug the rock out of this soil and constructed the wall that today they were about to demolish. Clear to him beyond the years were men, sweating under the lash, manacled and bleeding, building the great wall, the age-old and useless wall that formed a barrier behind him. He could see those men of the mines of Dannemora, grim figures out of the past, and he could look at his own men. And he was not afraid.

Today they were his.

"Men," he said, "you are going to do what every inmate in the world wants to do. You are going to demolish a prison wall. A century ago men dug these rocks out of the mountain, and shackled, ankle to ankle, piled them against their freedom.

"Blood and sweat stained those rocks. They told those men, as they tell you, that there was no escape from Dannemora.

"These rocks were sentinels of the damned. But temples before this have risen on ruins; from these stones, also, shall rise a shrine which you will build; from the despair of years you shall erect a temple to your strength and to your courage for yourselves and for generations yet to come. Build up the

temple of God, not only one made by hands, but another—the
temple of God which is yourselves, that you may rise as this
church is rising, into manhood, which is your birthright, which
dungeons cannot defeat nor all gates and rocks in the world
bar you from.

"Build it for Saint Dismas, the thief who broke into heaven
from the cross. Build it for the promise of paradise that was
given to you through him. Build it because for three days
before the first of the just, the righteous, were led by the ransom of Christ into heaven, Dismas alone, the thief alone, of all
the human race, Dismas alone dwelt in the glory of God.

"Take down these stones, quarried of your blood and your
despair and your misery, and build them up again unto hope
in the redemption of Christ!

"They tell you there is no escape from the walls of Dannemora. Then I tell you to build an escape for yourselves *inside*
the walls of Dannemora.

"Men! Tear down the walls!"

2.   Father Hyland was worried about Bud Horne. Perhaps,
of all the men, he had spoiled him, but he had regretted that
the very first time after his decision to ask the men to work he
had had to veto Horne's great plans for a fund-raising campaign. He had been trying to make it up to him. When he had
finally broken it to him, Horne had merely come in, laid the
bulk of manuscript on the desk, together with a copy of the
work sheet, and had looked at the priest through solemn
spectacles.

"Then I'd like to go on the building crew," he said.

Dominic had made the same request several times. Cassidy
had insinuated it. But of the four men in the office Bud Horne
was the most efficient and it would not be good to lose him.

"I need you here, Bud," he said. "You're overworked as it is.
And before I went to the hospital—wasn't I thinking of having
someone in to help you? What happened to that?"

"I don't remember."

That was strange. Bud Horne remembered everything.

"I know. It was Allan Green. Why wasn't he sent here?" The priest knew now why Greeney of all the men in the prison had looked at him reproachfully at first when they had met, and finally sullenly. He had promised to have him transferred to his office crew. "Don't you remember that?"

"I do now. I guess I slipped up."

If so, the priest thought, it's the first and only time. "All right. I'll get him myself. But I don't want to lose you, Bud."

"I could work part time," he said. "I figure I could start the office work in the morning and finish it in my cell. Then I got another idea—I want to write up the building of the church. I've got to see it to do that."

That was reasonable, and yet it was said with so little enthusiasm that Father Hyland could not think that Horne had the slightest interest in the church.

"All right. You can," he said.

"Thanks." Horne went into his own office.

Was he spoiling him, allowing him to do exactly as he wished? Yet this might be the way. Show him that he had confidence in him. Give him everything he asked for. Perhaps gratitude might be an opening wedge toward trust.

The priest would not have been quite so optimistic about his methods had he heard Horne in the outer office after he had left for the hospital. Horne said, "Cassidy—you know what? The boss wouldn't let you work on the project, would he?"

"No," Cassidy said. "I asked him. He gave me a stall."

"You don't play it right."

"You mean he's letting you?"

"Sure. I keep him worried."

He knew his game. Nothing could touch him. Cassidy went off sore. And he could make Dominic fume in the morning.

But in the morning something else happened. When the guard had let him in, earlier than the others, so that he could get the work started, he had found Pete dead in his cage, his little toes turned up, pink.

When Father Hyland came in he discovered Horne, for the

first time, embarrassed, attempting to push a cigar box which he had been tinkering with into a desk drawer.

"Hello, Horne," he said. "What have you got there?"

"Nothing."

"O.K." He started to go into his office when Bud stopped him.

"Pete's dead," he said.

"That's too bad," the priest replied much too lightly. "We'll have to give him a Christian burial." He passed on into the office.

Bud Horne took the cigar box out of his desk. He had lined it with cotton and silk and had laid Pete in it. He was ready now to begin on the decoration of the outside. The work on the church could wait.

And the chaplain didn't understand. It didn't mean anything to him that Pete was dead. What did he know about prisoners? What would he ever know about what birds meant?

3.   Brendon O'Malley was restive again. He had had nothing to do for so long, except to lie in the sun and sweat and grow fat and let the casts itch on his leg and arm. Once he had been irritated when the Señora looked at him with a half-smile.

"Why don't you look somewhere else? I'm not very pretty."

She laughed and went away.

He was bound here, a prisoner, growing gross with confinement and helplessness. Months of his youth were disappearing and he was jealous of the lost time. If only he could walk across the garden—ten steps.

Someday this will only be a bad dream. It won't seem real.

Why couldn't it have been his left arm? This way he couldn't even write his mother, reassuring her. The pen trembled, the letters were illegible. And why did she have to be a nurse and know all the things that could be wrong with him?

He was trapped here.

Then he saw the birds. He hated them because they hopped around, crippled, on the ground, when they had wings to fly.

He had never thought much about birds before. Now they were a symbol of all lost freedom.

He wanted to fly again.

4. The reason why Father Hyland had seemed to be unsympathetic about Pete's demise was that he had been distracted. The death of the bishop had put a new complexion on things and he probably would be called in soon to give an accounting. There certainly was not enough money to guarantee construction, and even the arguments about free labor and stone from the old walls sounded thin as he reviewed them.

But that was not all. It was this hospital affair. There, he was relying more and more on Tom Riordan's judgment, not only in the matter of books for the prisoners but on individuals and their needs.

This was the case of the lad from Puerto Rico who was supposed to have St. Vitus's dance and epilepsy. He had seen him in a fit. It was pretty bad.

That was in the confined area—walls of the cells fourteen feet high before even a window, utterly bare, no mattress, no clothing. Naked things groveling, screaming, or sunk down in apathetic misery. And this boy was the worst of all.

He was coal-black and he seemed to have no joints, so that as the attendants peered at him through the shutter, watching his naked body writhe and squirm, there seemed to be only a mass of black snakes, angry and contorted.

But weirdest of all, his fingernails were a chalk-white—all the nail except for a pale moon of pink. They were in ghastly contrast with his ebony and one would watch them fascinated as they writhed.

The guard had seen it too often to be moved. "He's worse when you come around, Padre," he said flatly.

It was that which made him think and to bring the subject up with Tom Riordan.

"If you don't mind, Father," Tom said, "I haven't mentioned this to anyone. They'd think I was—crazy."

"I don't mind. What is it?"

"I don't think that boy has any of the things they say he has."

"You don't?"

"No. But they wouldn't believe me if I told them. Maybe you won't."

"Maybe not. Why don't you try?"

"I think—perhaps—he's possessed."

Not in this day and age. It didn't happen here. The priest believed implicitly in its possibility, but he felt about it almost as he did about miracles—that the natural explanations must be sought first and only if one were convinced beyond doubt, scientifically, that there was no natural reason, could one accept the miraculous. Perhaps, after all, Tom was having aberrations.

"We mustn't be sure of that, Tom," he said quietly.

"I know. I'm not sure. But I've seen things."

"Such as what?"

"Just that he never has these fits unless you come around. Or unless something else like that happens. I mean—coming near a crucifix. And once I——"

"Yes. Go on."

"I gave him a holy medal. He took it and he hung it around his neck. It happened then. You've seen him in those—fits."

The priest had seen him. He need not take Tom's word for it, of course, but all through that night and into the following morning he was wondering amid nightmare if perhaps in this materialistic age there were not things labeled otherwise by the psychiatrists and catalogued differently by the medics which were not simple, downright occurrences of old-fashioned demoniac possession.

The thought gnawed at his consciousness. It was no wonder that he could not be quite as sympathetic as he might have been over the death of a canary.

5. In the streaming light of the galleries that early spring evening Max Bergner felt himself in darkness. The savor had gone out of his prayer and all the joy which he had felt, the companionship which he had known with the communion of

saints in heaven, and the union he had experienced with God, were all gone.

He felt cut off from everything. For years now he had practiced detachment from the things around him, allowing them only to enter into his prayer, where he could refer them all to God. He did not mind this kind of solitude. He had cherished it as long as he could live his anchorite life amid this horde of people and maintain his unimpassioned love for them, keeping them in his prayers.

He had brought the world in here. There were times when he had thought that he had forgotten no one. As a sinner of sinners he had been joined to all the humanity of the world, and his expiation had never been for himself alone, but for all for whom Christ had died. Moments had come when he had so united himself to the Good Thief on the cross that he had felt one with him, not as if Christ were offering him immediate redemption, but as if he, the symbolic sinner of the world, could reaffirm with Dismas the strong faith he had in the divinity.

It was all gone now. There was no nearness of Christ to promise him anything. The long vigils, the prayer, the intimate living with the Holy Ghost about him had been taken from him.

Sometimes his mind would shout at him, "You are losing the Faith." Sometimes he would have doubts about his whole course of asceticism, thinking that in avoiding the distraction of companions he had falsely cut himself off from the human race. But he knew that had not been so.

Why was this? His prayers had been answered and there was the beginning of the church. There was a better feeling among the men, and he had prayed for that too. But God, in the very act of being good to him, had deserted him. He was all alone on his cross, with Christ dead beside him, and the last memory of the words rolling between the hills, "My God, my God, why hast Thou forsaken me?"

Max Bergner, resolving to see the priest in the morning, knelt when the lights went out and said the words of prayer

which he felt to be empty all through the solitary night.
"Deliver us from evil," he prayed.
"Lead us not into temptation."
The presence of Satan was a felt thing all about him.

6. Greeney had joined the office staff, and his devotion was
almost embarrassing. He dogged the priest's footsteps like a
devoted puppy, and seemed to be content with a word or a
smile. Even the silent treatment administered to him by Bud
Horne, who obviously resented his presence, did not bother
him in the slightest. Besides, Horne was out of the office most
of the day now, working on the church, and he ought to be
satisfied. Certainly Greeney was.

"Happy, Greeney?" Father Hyland asked.
"You bet."
"Thought I'd let you down, didn't you?"
"Sort of."
"I was a little sick, remember? Things slipped up on me.
And you know what made me think of you finally?"
"Nope."
"Well, one day I was working down here in the office and I
heard a funny noise. First, I couldn't make it out. Then I got
it. Know what it was? It was a chin scraping. I heard it all the
way from E Block. I said to myself, 'Somebody's chin is
scraping the floor.' Then I listened, and I said, 'That's
Greeney's chin!' And it was. Now you never let me hear that
old chin of yours scrape again. All right?"
"You bet, Father."
Yes. There was a difference in the office. They all seemed to
be content except Dominic. He alone was sulking. Something
must be done for him. Obviously, as the early spring days became longer, and as Dominic could hear the sounds of the men
demolishing the wall, their shouts, the noise of stone on stone,
the business of office-routine clearly irked him more and more.

He flexed his muscles and wondered if he was getting soft.
He should be out there with the men, bossing them, showing
how to lift stones.

Dominic did not say anything because he had never asked a favor. If the padre couldn't tell what was the matter, there was something wrong with him. All he cared about now was the men who were tearing down the walls. He had forgotten Dominic. He did not have time for him—even to look at him and see how strong he was and where he should be. But Dominic had been his first friend in Dannemora. Who else had even spoken to him when he first came? Who had smiled at him? Not Cassidy. Not Martin. Certainly not Bud Horne.

Yet, before them all, the padre had preferred Cassidy to Dominic—had given Cassidy a great honor which Cassidy did not appreciate. Why should he have put Cassidy in charge of the Bambino?

It had happened like this.

One day a large bundle had arrived at the office. It had not been passed through inspection without a good deal of befuddled wonderment on the part of the investigators, for it seemed to contain a wide assortment of what looked like baby clothes, and very fancy ones at that. It was an odd thing to be addressed to the chaplain's office.

The prison officials had to be careful now too. The other day a man had requested yarn, because, he said, he wanted to knit. A silly request, but innocent enough. They let him have the yarn, and a couple of days later they had found him doped to the point of insensibility and a great deal of the dope-prepared yarn chewed up.

But what in the world could be the sinister purpose of fancy baby clothes? They let them through and determined to watch.

A few days later another large bundle came into the post office. It bore the same return address, "Mother Angela, Monastery of the Discalced Carmelites, Philadelphia, Pa."

And in it was a rather large doll, a strange doll with a crown on its head. Utterly baffled, the prison postal authorities let it through although certain remarks were passed in the households of Dannemora about the padre losing his mind and getting dolls for the prisoners to play with.

When Father Hyland saw the clothes and the doll he

laughed out loud, thinking of what utter confusion they must have caused. He unwrapped both parcels and set the Bambino up on his desk.

He must put someone in charge of it. Greeney wouldn't do. It would remind him too much of his own baby whom he had never seen. Bill Martin must be kept busy practicing the organ and getting the choir ready for some future day when there would be a cornerstone laying. Bud Horne. Perhaps. Bitter, dry, cold. But no. It would look too much like a sarcastic joke on him. He had no sense of humor. Dominic? Yes. Dominic would understand about the Bambino and would take loving care of it. But he would learn nothing from it. Dominic already knew all there was to know about devotion to the saints. It was in his tradition.

That left Cassidy. Good, hard-bitten, rough old Cassidy, who must somewhere or other have a soft spot under that graying hairy chest of his. He called him into the office.

"Cassidy," he said, "this is the Infant of Prague. I want you to have charge of it. It represents the Christ-child as King of the World and of all hearts. That's why it wears a crown. And it also means Christ reigning through all the Masses in the world—the King on our altars—so through all the seasons of the year this Christ-child wears the same colors as the priest at Mass. That's the meaning of the different clothes. Sometime this afternoon I'll teach you how to read this little pad I have here. We call it the *Ordo* and it tells what Mass to say and what you read in the breviary and what liturgical colors you wear. You'll have to learn how to read it and change the Infant's vestments every day. I want you to take charge of the Infant of Prague."

If Dominic could have seen Cassidy's reactions then he would not have worried about special privileges. For a moment Cassidy was silent, incredulous. Down from the hill came the sounds of the strong men with iron sledges on rock. Cassidy heard them and was shaken.

"You mean, Padre," he said brokenly. "You mean you want me to play nursemaid to a doll?"

7. Carlos Santa Cruz had been manufacturing more and more bills since Christmas. It seemed to him that every time he would start to get ahead, Mona would need more money. She had had large expenses in connection with the Turner trial to which at the last she had been called to testify, but it was a virtue in her, Carlos thought, to be so faithful to the man she loved.

Between himself and Mona everything had been kept on a business basis—always simple overpayments on her salary or quickly forgotten advances on her next pay check. There were presents, too, of course, but they were only in the way of bonuses. That kept up a dignity between them. He asked nothing in return, and he received only her coldness and sometimes her cruelty.

After a scene he would lie awake at night planning how to kill her, but it was with the same daydream quality in which he would fancy that she loved him and that they were married and living in a little place in Westchester or a flat in Brooklyn. These were dreams. The reality was that the next day he would find some way of giving her more money.

But now he was afraid. He had passed too many bills recently and he knew the government men were suspicious. With this new fear there came to him a sense of guilt which he had not had in a long time. He could not quite understand it. Even from the beginning he had not had any such feeling. Taking a few dollars from the government was a trifling thing in the face of political corruption and vast waste. That is what he had thought when he began to manufacture the bills. But now, oddly, it seemed wrong.

Well, he couldn't take such chances any more anyway. He would make one desperate effort to collect what Ruffino owed him. He would make Ruffino pay him.

It was the fury in him when Ruffino refused him his money, saying that the murals were no good and that he would not pay him a cent, that drove him to do what he did, and the growing fear and the resentment.

This time he did not think that he was right or that it did

not matter. When he forged Ruffino's name to the check he did it in cold blood. He hoped that it would hurt Ruffino. He wanted him to suffer.

It was only three days after he had cashed the check that he found the government men waiting for him in his studio. Mona was with them, and he knew. He made no pretenses. There was no use. He saw at once, from her eyes, what she had told them. Everything. The little printing press and the counterfeit bills. He had nothing to say to them—only to Mona.

"Why do you hate me?" he asked, puzzled; "I've done everything I could for you."

"Sure." Her face was made of flat planes; her nostrils were wide, Aztec. "Getting me into this mess—that's something."

Under the contempt in her eyes he could see her panic. He had been ready to be angry with her until he saw that, but then, when he understood, a pity came to him and a love, and he could not defend himself.

He understood. She had already been involved in a murder case—and now this. But there was still more.

"I know why you did it," he said. "I understand you—and please don't be afraid."

"Look here, you," she said. "You thought you could buy me off. I knew what you were doing. You couldn't even pay me to keep still. You couldn't buy me anyway——"

It was as if she had hit him across the mouth. He tasted blood on his tongue; in the pit of his stomach there was a gnawing like famine. How could she twist his love, which had demanded nothing of her, into briberies? How could she do this? She knew better. And then at last he understood her completely.

"I see," he said slowly. There were some people like her, who could not bear to accept things. The more you did for them the more you built up their resentment, their hatred. That had been the meaning of the scenes they had had, and he had been a fool, piling gift upon gift, building in her hatred. He had been a fool.

"I see," he said. "Gratitude is the hardest virtue."

"Virtue!" she cried. "Who are you to talk about virtue?" Her laughter was coarse.

"No one. But I can talk about love. I love you."

"Love!" she said. "Love! You scum!" She spat at him.

8.   The evening was more like March than like May. The great cloud was battered across the northern sky by the wind. Whiteface Mountain, far to the south, had its new green spattered by shadow. Even the sunset was chilly and intermittent with the long metal-gold clouds whisking across and interrupting it.

The two men standing on the torn hillside were also battered by the wind—the wings of the priest's great cloak flying out behind him, the warden's overcoat billowing with each fresh blast.

Below them, in an enormous jumble, sprawled the gigantic buildings, darkening, etched with light, as the cloud raced over. Immediately before them was still the great black cut in the ground and around them the ruins of a gigantic wall.

"There it is," the warden said. "That's what I'm leaving."

He looked down silently. The new brick of the infirmary brightened as if with a spotlight, darkened again, as the ray centered on the auditorium, then on the playing fields, then passed on, leaving only the foundations of the church in blackness.

"You've got to finish it. Padre," he said, "I know you haven't much money, but now you've started, it's got to be done."

"You know I'll do it."

"Yes. I know. I won't be here to see it, but Snyder is a good man. He'll see you through when I'm gone."

"I know what it will be," the priest said, wrapping his cloak about him. "It will always be like tonight. Sun and shadow. Things built and things still holes in the ground. I'm ready."

"Thank God," the warden said. "You've learned a lot since you came here."

"The men taught me."

"I think they did. But you're a rare man. You know how to learn."

"Thanks. And I owe you a great deal."

"That's nice to hear." The wind whipped the next words from his lips, but he was going on, ". . . and of all the things I've had any share in, this is where my heart is." He pointed down to the excavation. "I'm keeping this one hope for my own. You will do it, won't you? There will be a church here?"

"Yes," the priest said. "There will. I stood here once before when there was only a pit full of water. It is better now. There is a foundation."

"I'll never see it," the warden said, "but thank God you'll be around to see your work completed."

"No, never," the priest replied. "The church isn't the completion—it's the beginning. There'll be more!"

"What more?"

For a moment the landscape was all gray, and then one shaft of light broke through, illuminating the two figures standing on the mountain.

"There'll be men," the priest said.

CHAPTER THREE

From where he sat at his wheezy little organ in the auditorium Bill Martin could not see the men working on the hill, and soon he could not hear them. The stone wall was down, the slabs salvaged with the mortar cut away from them. Martin knew that Bud Horne believed a church would rise from that foundation. Once he had dreamed it. He laughed at that. He was more hard-boiled than Bud Horne.

There was the new auditorium that the Protestants were moving into tomorrow. That would do for the Catholics too. There was all the building program—the huge new infirmary unit, the beginning of a playing field, the first steps toward landscaping.

It was spring. Everything was rising—nature and the work

of men. And with the work there was a new spirit in the place. But though he had been the first of the men to believe in the church, he did not do so any longer. He had seen the books. There wasn't any money.

All he wanted to do anyway was to practice the organ, though he did wish that there were a larger one for his use. He was training a choir, and he enjoyed it. While the others were busy with their schemes he could be building a thing that they could not stop—a music that would go on as long as he would be here—his life.

If only he knew more! His education had been limited—a few piano lessons from a nun when he was a boy, a naturally light but true voice, and lately, with practice, an ability to read more than simple hymn tunes. There had been no one to teach him, but in the last week or two he had been hearing that a musician had come to Clinton Prison, and maybe he would help. That is why he had stopped practicing. He had seen Cyrus Turner playing checkers in the far corner of the hall.

Slowly he closed his copy of *Largo* and slid off the bench, ambling over casually to the checker players. He saw Turner's big hands moving deftly over the board—three jumps with his king and the game almost over.

When it was through, and Turner stood up, Bill Martin spoke to him.

"You know music," he said. "I want you should teach me."

Turner did not look at him. He swept the checkers together into the middle of the board and said "No."

So there was nothing to be done here. If he were outside for one week he could get to someone who knew about these things.

There was a way to get out for a few days. Someone at home would have to be sick. He hadn't thought much about home recently, hadn't let himself, and there was all the family to face, his sister's children whom he had never seen, and all. There was his father. He was getting old. He'd have to be sick sometime, wouldn't he?

Home wouldn't be the same, of course, but as he folded up

his music sheets to go back and report in the office, he remembered. He wanted to sit beside the kitchen stove and eat onion soup with little pieces of fried bread in it. Funny. He hadn't thought of that at all in twenty-two years.

No. That wasn't what he wanted. He wanted to get out so someone could tell him about music. That was his reason.

Back in the office he found Cassidy dressing his doll in its next-day's clothes. Cassidy had not heard him come in, and he was rather sheepish about getting caught, looking pleased, smoothing out into perfect folds the white satin skirt and patting into place the stiffly brocaded gold cape of the little King.

"O.K., Butch," he said to the Infant, ignoring Martin. "I guess that will hold you."

"What did you call him?" Martin asked.

"Butch," Cassidy said. "Little Butch." Then he added belligerently, "I guess if Bud can have his boids I can have Butch." He placed the Bambino in its niche—its crown only slightly askew. "And you can have your sing fests, and we'll all be one big happy Italian family."

"Yeah. Except Dominic. What's he got?"

"Everybody's got something," Cassidy said philosophically. "Yeah. Everybody."

Father Hyland came in then, and heard that. Yes. Thank God everybody had something, and it made a difference. Already one could feel it. They were making their lives in prison. It was an important step—one which he must meditate on and use. There were years of their lives to be spent here. The men must be made to accept them, not as marking time until released, but as valuable in themselves. What was it that kept Tom Riordan sane amid the mental unfit, except his plans for the library? A future, and a hope for things within the walls, not only after release.

He had been thinking. He had not noticed that Bill Martin was waiting to speak to him.

"I didn't see you standing there."

"That's all right. I just want to tell you my father's sick and I'm going to see him."

"That's too bad. Can I help you?"

"No. I'm just telling you."

"I see. You know the regulations?"

"Sure." He knew. He knew every angle. You could go once
—either when a parent was sick or when he was dead. Not
both times. Sure. He knew. He wanted to go now.

"All right. Anything I can do?"

"Nope. I'm just telling you."

"Thanks."

Bill Martin turned and strode out the door.

Well, that was that, the priest thought. Once he had failed
him, when he was in solitary, and the aid had come, the defense had come, too late. It would take a long time——

Then he laughed at the irony of the situation. What had he
just been thinking? That he was beginning to find the way to
build up the man's interest in things inside the gates, and here,
at the very same instant, Bill Martin, whom he had been sure
was satisfied with the progress of his choir, had only one
thought—to be out of here.

What he did not know would have consoled him. Bill
Martin, on the way back to cell inspection and the counting
before supper, was thinking, "I'll get out for a few days and I'll
get books to be sent in, and then I can work all my life—all my
time right here—and I'll have a secret life that nobody will
know about—right here inside the gates."

2. The publicity, the publicity. It was driving Carlos Santa
Cruz crazy. They were crying his name in the subways—this
fool who had been such a clever counterfeiter, turning forger,
and being caught on all counts. How he had signed Ruffino's
name to a check; how his girl had turned against him—everything. All his friends knew.

At the trial they were pitiless. The witnesses kept back
nothing about him on the stand. No one should have to experience this nakedness until the judgment day. There would
be no secret place in his heart left unexposed, and it was not

right for any mortal man to bear it—the things Mona said about him and his way with her.

If any of it had been false he could have borne it. But it was all true. What could you do against truth? There was no defense against it, no way in which you would keep an inner integrity, saying to yourself that no matter what anyone said or thought, you yourself had a core of being, a verity which they could not touch. He was all exposed. There was nothing left within him.

And now he would be sent to Clinton Prison, Dannemora, where for years there would be eyes watching him, espionage, guards, the quick look back over the shoulder to see that there was no one sneaking up behind; living with a thousand others, being circumspect in act and word, even in expression, lest a look betray him.

He, who had lived the free Bohemian life. He who had scorned public opinion, laughing at the ridiculous Philistines who criticized him. He who had been in the great tradition of the Individuals.

Some place, some place in his heart, he must keep for his own.

3. The distracting little annoyances that came made Father Hyland impatient. There were the big things to be done, for the church and for the men, and now this stupid column in the New York paper would doubtlessly cause waste energy. He had picked it up in his box at the Administration Building along with the tabs that came every day from the men. It was a clever little piece, very clever indeed, recounting the anecdote that he had told months ago, about Lucky Luciano and the numbers racket.

No doubt it had been well meant. And he certainly had told it. But it had been in a private gathering of friends and no one with any sense would publish it. He would have to explain to the new warden and to the new bishop, and that wasn't going to be easy.

Oh well. He had more important things. There were these

cases, each one a lifetime matter, scrawled on torn paper. He must attend to them—give them all his attention.

There was this first one now.

Reverend Hilan:

Pardon me for disrespec by these lines. I am here 29 years by Mr. Morgan and not for Crime. I am Mario Morelli who are charged for kidnapping and murder of that lovely child of Joseph Veratti of no. 354 East 13 St.—New York City in which I tried and convicted to die, in the electric chair.

It is I proved in courte by bookeper of building company. I work and I prove too by State Doc. who are found the lovely child, death. he said I am in Jail 5 day before child are killed. I was in all world and never seemed black hand and bandits like people in New York State. *Se la madre del cameni, scoltasse le mei prechierei allora si, tutto il poor saliscie encilie.*

Mario Morelli

Here was Bill Martin's request for a visit to his dying father. He countersigned that and put it in the wicker basket. Here was another letter—sick children, rent overdue, no means of cooking or washing, son recently convicted and sent to reform school. Must look into that.

Another—Greeney's wife was suing for divorce. Had he been neglecting Greeney a bit lately?

Another—Carlos Santa Cruz, recently arrived, would like an interview.

Max Bergner requesting an interview. What could he want? Of all the men he seemed most settled.

Then there was still the pile of letters from contractors, teachers, masons, and an important one from the union. That might mean trouble. He tore it open hastily, remembering that he had been warned unions might object to prison labor. For a moment he put the letter aside, unread. That could wait. He must tackle the personal problems first. Now take Morelli—he asked for nothing, merely stating his case, but no doubt he thought that that was all that was necessary and the padre would do the rest. But he was strict with his principles—he would do nothing to interfere with prison routine, attempt to regulate sentences. There were injustices, he knew, but he was no lawyer and he disliked the idea of amateur interference. He would see Morelli anyway.

This family situation was simpler. He could have the rent paid and have someone interview the wayward son and send a report. He started to draft a letter about it when the phone rang.

Greeney came to the door, a Greeney who had heard about his wife, a Greeney with lackluster eyes.

"It's the bishop, Padre," he said.

So. It hadn't taken His Excellency long to find out about the column. Father Hyland gave himself a few seconds to prepare an explanation. Then he picked up his own phone.

It was not the bishop after all. It was the episcopal secretary.

"I'm sorry to disturb you," the metallic voice said, "but His Excellency is trying to arrange his program. We have an annotation here that calls for the laying of your cornerstone on July 23. Does that still hold?"

"Certainly. Why shouldn't it?"

"Just making sure. They say there's opposition from outside."

"I suppose there is." His hand reached out for the letter from the union, and he wished that he had read it before this call came through. "I have a letter from the union here——" he began.

"Oh?" It was a question. "We hadn't heard about that. Is there trouble there too?"

Put his foot in it, the priest thought. With his left hand he fumblingly unfolded the letter, looking at it rapidly.

"No," he said with relief. "On the contrary. That was just a false alarm—this letter here—it's a very nice letter—says the union will back us all the way—says they will allow their men to help because we're financed by charity. No opposition at all."

"That's good. But how about this other thing?"

Here it comes. Now for that stupid column.

"What other thing?"

"This opposition movement I was just talking about. If they

stop you, you can't have the cornerstone, can you? The bishop will have to rearrange his schedule."

There was the perfectly efficient secretary—worrying about the bishop's schedule when the important thing was the cornerstone, the church.

"I don't know a thing about that," Father Hyland replied. "It can't be very important or I'd know it."

"All right. As long as you're going through with it."

"Yes," he said emphatically. "I'm going through with it."

When he had hung up, Greeney was waiting again.

"Warden Snyder has been trying to get you, Father."

So. This was it. He picked up his own phone and got the warden. Just as he expected, the warden wanted to see him at once on urgent matters. On the way down to the warden's office he kept thinking of innumerable objections that the officials could have to that column. Betraying prison secrets. Ridiculing official custody. Implying a score of things—but he would try to have answers ready for them all.

4.   When he had gone, Greeney tried to put some order into the chaplain's desk. It was a hard job, with the papers strewn about the way they were, but someday Pop would notice what had been done. Greeney knew he wasn't very good at talking and that he didn't have enough words, so that it was hard for him to say things the way Bud Horne could. He never said the right thing. All he could do was straighten up the office, keep things looking right. He could carry the padre's bags to the inner gate where the guard stood—be watching in the morning for the padre to come, so that he could get the bag from him.

It was all that he had left now. Millie was gone for good—and the baby. Of course his brother hadn't come to see him again after last time.

He had been happy when he had been chosen for the job in the office. Then the padre had talked to him often, about home and his sentence and the way he was serving time for something he didn't do. Once the padre had said, "Greeney, did you ever do a wrong thing in your life?"—just as if he didn't know from his confessions, and Greeney had said he had done a lot of wrong things.

"Then maybe this is the answer," Father Hyland had told him. "Maybe you can take this for what you have done, things nobody caught you at except God."

Gee, that had helped. It didn't seem so unjust any more, but lately he had to keep going on the recollection of such things. Pop seemed never to notice that he was around. He might just as well be a piece of furniture. And now with Millie gone there wasn't anybody else. There was just Pop.

"Damn it!" he thought, giving another wipe to the window-panes that were already glistening. "I could just drop dead right here and he wouldn't even notice it. I could be dead in front of him and he wouldn't even see me."

5. With his arguments marshaled, Father Hyland waited for a mention of Lucky Luciano. It was not forthcoming.

"There's something very serious here," Warden Snyder said. "It seems a committee has been formed—calls itself the 'New York League for the Separation of Church and State.' It has served an injunction on the Department of Correction against the building of the church. That's bad."

"They can't do that," Father Hyland exclaimed. "We have permission from the governor—Commissioner Mulrooney——"

"Padre," the warden said kindly, "what have you got in writing?"

"Why—I——" It had never dawned on him. Nothing in writing. Not a word.

"See what I mean? Even when you've built it, your church won't exist. It just isn't. That was the way they planned it. Officially, there never was to be a church within prison walls— no matter how big you built it. And now—all they have to say to this League is that no official approval has ever been given. What have you got? A foundation—some plans—not much money, have you?"

"Not much—yet."

"Popular support? A little. Those Dempster MacMurphy articles that have been appearing have helped you there. But you need publicity. More people have got to know about this project."

Here was irony. This morning he had had publicity and had been afraid of it. Now the warden wanted more.

"There was something in a New York column——" the priest said hesitantly.

"Yes. I saw that. Pretty clever stuff too. You need more like that if we're going to stop this League." He paused for a moment. "Did you notice I said 'we'? That means I'm in back of you. I'm only temporary around here, and I'm trying to do everything according to Warden Murphy's plans. Your project was the biggest thing he had in mind. So if you're willing we're going to fight. Go ahead with the cornerstone. That'll bring some publicity all right—and make those bigots as sore as hornets. Will you go along with me?"

"I will, sir," he said, "all the way. We'll fight."

"But get the idea—it's going to be tough. Here—you'd better have this."

He tossed over a copy of the injunction. It was stiffly and legalistically worded.

"I don't see how this gives us much out," Father Hyland said. "We can't very well go on building with this thing against us now."

"No. But I don't see that it will stop you from putting mortar around a cornerstone. And it won't stop the schools or the other projects. Winter will be here anyway, and most of the work will have to be done indoors. In the meantime, keep going with the schools. You've killed the idle-company menace. You've got to make people realize that."

Together they went over to the window. To their left men were working on the concrete tables of the new yard. To the right, beyond the wall, there was a scene which could only have been duplicated in the Middle Ages. Booths of all kinds set up, each with its specialized function—lathers, masons, bricklayers, stonecutters, carpenters—each with an inmate instructor who had learned his craft in the schools. Unseen in the building other schools were going on now.

"It's different from when you first came here, isn't it?" Warden Snyder asked.

"Yes, thank God."

"And they told me there'd be trouble with the tools."

"They told me that too."

"There hasn't been and there won't be."

"No. I don't think so."

"You've found the answer, Padre. Right out there——"

Father Hyland was silent for a moment. "Not quite all the answer. Not quite yet."

"What do you mean?"

"I mean we've got men at work, with interest—with a purpose in life. We've got more volunteers than we can use. Something has spread through the rest of the prison. But we still haven't got at the men as individuals. They're just machines—still just numbers——"

"You can't do everything," the warden began.

"I've got it!" the priest cried suddenly. "It'll slow the work—and that's good; it'll take us a year longer, but we'd be delayed anyhow; and it'll give more time to talk to them as human beings. I've got it!"

"What's the matter with you now?"

"Coffee hour! We'll have a coffee hour every day—twice a day. Let them knock off for a while in the morning and in the afternoon. That's the answer! Then I can spend that time with them."

"It'll be expensive."

Dick Ryan! He'll help. And——

"I don't care about that—if it costs more than the concrete. It's too important."

"Look, Padre, you do anything you like. All I have to do is look out my window and say to myself I didn't believe in your crazy scheme once. That's humbling enough. So go ahead. When will you start?"

"Now," the priest called, already at the door. "Right now."

And a few minutes later he was in the office, shouting for Greeney.

"Come here!" he called. "I'm putting you in charge of the biggest thing yet. You and I, Greeney—you're going to feed two or three hundred men. You're going to cheer them up—make 'em happy. You and I. We're going to make human beings out of that mob out there, see?"

He outlined his plan then and saw the comprehension of it come to Greeney.

"You and I?" Greeney asked, and then very boldly, "You and I, Pop?" He had said it, and the padre wasn't angry.

"Yes," he replied. "You and I—kid. Will you help me with it?"

And all Greeney could say was, "Pop!"

CHAPTER FOUR

There had been a movie that afternoon, and all around him Carlos Santa Cruz had heard the laughter, coming through the darkness, and the applause when it was over beat upon him like waves. The picture had been vastly appreciated—Edward G. Robinson in *Brother Orchid*—and the population had cheered when it was over.

He had been satisfied with the darkness, the two hours' isolation. Only for a few moments had he been able to follow what was going on on the screen. The rest was a blur, filled in by his own thoughts retreating from the distraction of the story.

That was the way it was all the time. He had tried to paint, but he could not paint here, thinking, thinking, the fear like a wind in his belly, like a blood smear before his vision. Everything that he had had joy in seemed to have twisted against him. His legs were weak with the thought and he wanted to sleep all the time, because when he was asleep there would be a part of him to tell him that dreams were dreams—not so bad as reality.

Outside, when something went wrong, you had to cover it up. You had to smile and talk and carry on—go places. You could even get drunk. But in here there was no reason for anything. He would know no one in this place.

Outside, you could go to your studio and daub a canvas or two and feel better. He had thought that he might be able to do that here, but he couldn't think, could he? He couldn't see. And there was only room for one feeling. One at a time. The feeling that filled him body and soul. Round and round. He was a cage and there were rats in him.

How much can I take? There is no one to talk to. How much can a mind stand?

As he was coming out of the auditorium a guard touched Santa Cruz on the shoulder. "Santa Claus," he said, "you're wanted at the chaplain's office. Come along with me."

They marched together, the fear knotting inside Santa Cruz. He had asked for this interview, but now he did not want to talk even to a priest. Would it be like this with a mother whose child wanted to be born, a physical pain to be free of it, a tightening of heart to keep it still within herself? How could he expose this thing which had been his life to any other mortal?

For the first time since he had come to prison the guard left him alone. He was alone with the priest. He was a tired priest —a priest whose eyes had seen too much. It was not good, Carlos said to himself, to have eyes like that. Such eyes could not be surprised. They could flash with anger. They could brighten with enthusiasm. But then their sight could turn inward upon self, as now his own sight had turned inward. Then they would be eyes you would not wish to paint.

The introductions were formally friendly, but he was still talking through a mist, his words having no relation to his thinking, wishing that the priest's eyes could read his mind, as at moments he thought they could. But he must plunge in and be bold. He must talk.

"What I am angry with myself for," he said, "is that I was stupid. I was a very clever counterfeiter, and, as it turned out, I was well covered. You see, I was all ready with fences and angles and everything. I had a good story. They couldn't have got me. Only then I did something else. I am not a good forger. So they got me for that. And I wasn't expecting it."

It sounded weak. Silly. These were not the words he wanted.

No wonder the priest was laughing. But he was not, he noticed, laughing at him. More as if he were laughing at himself.

"That's funny you should say that." Father Hyland smiled. "I had almost the same experience today." He told him briefly, humorously, how he had been ready to defend himself about the newspaper column and how something much more serious had come up, for which he was not prepared at all.

"That's always the way it seems to be," he concluded. "The things you are ready for won't happen. Now you"—he said seriously—"you were ready to be defiant if you ever were caught. And instead of that it's backed up on you very differently, hasn't it?"

"Oh yes," Carlos answered. "If I could only get mad."

"Yes. That helps sometimes. Or if you could only talk."

"Do you know I want to talk?"

"Yes. You do, don't you?"

"But I can't, you see."

"I think you can. But not to me—or anyone—this way. There's only one way you can talk now." He got up and closed the door. "You can talk in confession. Then it's just as if there were nobody here—only an ear, and the listening of God. Now kneel down."

It was a long confession—half an hour of pouring out all the past, straightening out even the warped thinking that had made his counterfeiting seem somehow right and his forgery blacker than it was. Straightening out even his previously uncertain desires for Mona, which he had thought noble because he had never acted upon them. Getting down below the maggots in his mind to the sound place that was his heart, but above all talking, talking, talking—until it seemed that it did not matter what advice the priest gave, and in truth he gave very little, because just talking about it there within the sacrament made things clear and straight of themselves.

There was nothing like it in the world! Even a psychiatrist might reveal to someone what you had said, but this priest, with the purple ribbon around his neck, must die rather than reveal. Nor was it like talking to yourself, or like trying to talk directly to God. God had made men to be talked to, to listen, to understand, to question, as God would not do Himself, and then to be forever silent. Only God would have thought of this, and no human medicine could replace it.

When he stood up after the absolution and the blessing, for the first time he began to breathe. There was air that he could take into his lungs, clean, crisp air. He hadn't known that he had not breathed before.

Going out with the priest, who was to begin his rounds of the galleries, it was dark, but he could see quite clearly. When the guard waited to take him back to his cell, he saw the tall priest forever invested with his secret, going to others, collecting within his silent mind all the horrors of the world and having them cleansed there by the white fire of his spirit.

Going on——

The first cell at which Father Hyland stopped housed Lee Sapis Robinson. The man had puzzled him. He had always seen him at Mass but he knew that he was not a Catholic, probably nothing. He had a proper fear of being accused of proselytizing, but it would do no harm to ask questions— give the man an opportunity.

"Lee," he said, "I'm starting a convert class soon. You're too late for the baptisms we're going to have, before the cornerstone is laid, but right after that I'm beginning another class. Would you like to join?"

Lee Sapis Robinson smiled toothily. "I guess I'm just too dumb," he said.

"I'm not forcing you. I just thought—you've been coming to church all the time. I thought you might like to be a Catholic."

"I don't think I'm good enough."

"I'm not so good myself, Lee," he said. "Just that the faith helps me to be better. It might work with you."

"I will sometime, Padre. Just you watch. You'll catch me yet." He laughed, and the priest passed on.

He had intended to get to Morelli's cell as quickly as he could, but someone whom he had never seen before, a fairly new prisoner, called to him. The first thing that the priest noticed was the size of the hands that gripped the bars, and the second that this man was a gentleman. There was no mistaking it even here, even before he spoke. There was a fineness in him as well as strength.

"I'm Cyrus Turner, Father," he said, like one who was accustomed to having the name recognized. "I have a rather odd request. I'd like a few bars of soap and the use of a clasp knife."

As chaplain he had heard strange requests before, but this was the strangest. He said so.

"I know it sounds rather peculiar," Turner said. "You see I'd like to do some sculpture. I'd like to begin with small pieces."

"Are you a sculptor?"

"No. I know nothing about it. And I realize the difficulties. Ultimately I am going to ask for heavy blocks of marble, chisels—all the impossible things. Everyone is going to think I have some sinister purpose. I haven't. I expect you to believe me."

"I do believe you."

"Good. Then I'll show you these things."

There were two or three small carvings made out of chips of soap—weird, grotesque, and almost impossibly delicate.

"This is just to show that I mean it."

"But how did you do these things?"

"With a common pin. I might do better with a knife."

"Yes," the priest said. Chisels, hammers, blocks of marble, but those could come later. Now there was need only for bars of soap and a clasp knife.

"I'll get them for you," he said. "You'll have them in the morning."

He started to turn away, but Turner called after him.

"Father—just a moment. I want to tell you something else. The other day that organist of yours asked me to teach him. I said no. I'm sorry I was so abrupt, but I want you to know that I have made that sacrifice. I shall never play again. You see——"

Now Father Hyland remembered. Turner. Cyrus Turner——

"You must, though," he said.

"No. That's final. Call it a kind of atonement if you will. I'm offering it for a very dear girl whom I thought I was in love with once. Her name was Mona. She was sufficiently involved with me, but something else came up. She got into trouble over a painter who, I understand, is here. I hope I never meet him. You see——"

And the priest heard, as if for the first time that night, a very different and a very false version of the story of Carlos Santa Cruz and Mona. He said nothing at all, nothing at all. But he kept thinking about it on his way back to his office.

There he sat down and began a long overdue letter to Mother Angela, referring to Mona and Santa Cruz and Turner only as a "Special Intention," then revealing everything about his worries, financial and legal. He told her all about his need for money and publicity—all about the League for the Separation of Church and State. He told her things that he told no one else, because once there had been a girl whom he had met when she was young and very beautiful.

He did not write her very often, but when he did, it was a pouring out of needs, of worries, from one who was the recipient of confidences of need and worry all day long, day after day.

Sometimes he needed someone himself.

There was Mother Angela.

On the morning of the cornerstone laying, just after he had assured himself that everything was ready—one corner of the church up, one window, the floor laid, the bishop's vesting place—Bill Martin announced that he was going to visit his father. He had been here twenty-three years and he was choosing this day of all days.

Even though Father Hyland had been chaplain now for more than four years, the irresponsibility of prisoners always came as a shock to him.

"You can't do that!" he said. "I signed for you to go some-time, but you've got to have the choir today. You've been working at it hard enough. We're expecting three bishops here. Who'll direct the music?"

"There's Cyrus Turner." Bill's face was a mask, but even in the flatness of his voice there was a sneer.

"He won't do it."

"No? That's too bad. He's a professional musician. I'm not. He's had a chance."

There was only the implication of self-pity under the words. But it was the key.

"Look, Bill," the priest said, "you haven't had a chance be-cause I haven't had a chance. I'm not going to have a church without an organ. And somehow we'll get you lessons."

He stopped. It sounded like bribery, and he did not intend to bribe Bill Martin or any other man. So he went on, "And if you want to go today, you can. I'll be able to conduct the choir myself. So you go off. And when you come back—you're still in the same position. Nothing's changed."

"O.K. If that's the way you feel about it. I'll stay."

"But you've made all the arrangements now. How can you stay?"

"That's up to you, Padre."

For the rest of the morning and into the early afternoon—when he should have been arranging for the thousand guests who were to be in attendance, for the class of seventy-one that he had prepared for confirmation, for the arrangements to be made for Father Morgan O'Brien, who was to be the guest preacher, for the three bishops—he was busy calling all the officials who needed to know, to get Bill Martin a delay order for twenty-four hours.

Yet somehow everything was done. Left to themselves, the

prisoners had done it. And it was about perfect, down to the last detail of striped awning and carpet, to cut flowers, even to Little Butch—he must not let himself get into the habit of thinking of the Infant as that—installed under a silken canopy, designed and executed by Cassidy. And next to the Infant's throne a chair for Father Hyland's mother, and beside the chair a grim and belligerent Cassidy, allowing no one else to sit there, except the guard, Joe Hogan, who owned it all, including——

Father Hyland rushed down the hill as fast as he could when he heard that not one but three bishops had already arrived. He was too late to greet them at the gate and found his own ordinary already deeply engrossed with Warden Snyder.

"I understand," the bishop said after he had entered, "that the State has Attorney Epstein to defend the Church against the League. What nationality would that be?"

"Jewish," Father Hyland said.

"Splendid. I like that. God bless whoever thought of it. Rabbi Schoenkopf to testify for you—and Warden Snyder—there should be no doubt about its being—let us say—not too exclusively Catholic."

Then Warden Snyder made a speech to the bishop. "Sir, any honest prison official would have to go along with it. This project has reduced our disciplinary problems to a minimum. And do you know that not one of the church gang has violated a single institutional law?"

"That's splendid," the bishop said. "Splendid."

Father Hyland could not resist breaking in. "Yes, it is. And it's also a miracle—since the warden sent me all the incorrigibles in Dannemora. You know you did!"

"I did," the warden said laughingly. "He made them corrigible, Bishop. I knew he would—just as I know he'll win now."

"You will win," the bishop agreed. "I couldn't afford to lay the cornerstone of a church that wouldn't exist. I believe in it absolutely. So now let us go up that atrocious mountain and show the League for the Separation of Church and State a little lesson in brotherly love between Church and State."

Whatever may have been thought by the many guests who came that afternoon about the whole business of separation, there was no doubt but that they were affected by the visible joy of the prisoners, deeply moved by the spectacle of so many kneeling before the bishop to be confirmed, reverent and stirred by the magnificent sermon which Father O'Brien gave.

For the first time in the history of the world a church was being erected within prison walls—to be built by prisoners, worshiped in by convicts, dedicated to a culprit. There was a moving glory about that day.

All through the ceremony Father Hyland had had one eye on Bill Martin. The choir was good and the wheezy organ did not sound as bad as it might. Martin, too, must be satisfied, even a bit proud, though his face was unresponsive; it was Bud Horne who seemed to be accepting congratulations as just tribute.

All in all it was a triumphant afternoon. And now that it was nearly over the sunset began in a great glory over the western Adirondacks—a sunset not like the other strange one when he had stood here in the months ago with Warden Murphy, but a great splendor and warmth over all the mountainside, catching the purple of the bishop's robe, softening to rose the gray, pathetically pressed uniforms of the prison population. A glorious sunset, and a fitting end.

But something else was happening. The band leader was approaching, even through the convict altar boys and by the bishop's entourage. Something he wanted.

"Yes?" the priest asked.

"We've got a special number we want to play. Can we?"

"Sure. Go ahead."

He did not know what it would be, and hoped that it would be all right. He was sure it would be—but——

The band, with the sunset gleaming on their brasses, the band that had gone through so much to shield a murderer in its number, the murderer back among them, struck up "The End of a Perfect Day."

Silly. Sentimental. But right! Eternally right.

And somehow it was not sentimental when, at the chorus, the choir wheeled about and sang as they never had sung before, and Father Hyland could see Bill Martin with the sunlight strong upon his face, the mask dropped, and an expression of radiant pride in his eyes.

When it was over and there was a congratulatory throng of civilians around him, one prisoner remained on the outskirts of the group. Father Hyland disengaged himself and went over to Bill Martin.

"O.K., Pop?" Bill asked.

"O.K.," the priest said.

CHAPTER FIVE

The building of the Church of the Good Thief did not stop, as both Father Hyland and Warden Snyder had been sure that it must. Mr. Epstein, the State's solicitor in Albany, assured them that the League's plea for injunction had no force until the case came to trial, and that if they wanted to risk the possibility of an adverse decision, they could proceed with their plans. The timbers were raised, and they made an occasion of that; and now the walls were rising and the church was taking shape. There was much publicity.

It was a Gothic building, one hundred and fifty-six by fifty-two feet, to seat twelve hundred persons. The tower, built of solid masonry, not steel, was to rise one hundred and twenty-five feet. Already you could see the outlines of it above the wall.

During that time the only injunction came not from outside the prison but from within. Some officious guard or other had objected to a tower. Couldn't an inmate swing out from it, board the wall, and escape? The work stopped for a day until the chaplain could bring the principal keeper to the site and show him the vast space between the tower and the wall. The principal keeper smiled.

"That's all right, Padre," he said. "Keep going. Not even Doug Fairbanks could make that leap." So they went ahead.

The coffee hours were even more successful than he had anticipated, and though he had been joking when he had said that even though they cost more than the cement he would have them, he found now that they were costing a great deal. Most of it came out of his own pocket. But between Greeney and himself so much was being accomplished.

Greeney would scurry about, noticing a sagging jaw here and listening to a complaint there. Difficulties that Father Hyland could not have discovered himself Greeney would light upon; and then, casually, the priest would stroll over to a booth or table and begin a conversation. Most problems, of course, he would uncover by himself. But he would give Greeney credit for them. It helped.

Here was Lee Sapis Robinson sifting sand for the cement, grinning at him when he came over. Not exactly to the chaplain's surprise, he had joined the instruction classes after the cornerstone celebration, but he had merely sat through them asking no questions.

"Lee," Father Hyland said now, "haven't you any difficulties at all about religion? You never ask me anything."

"No, sir," Robinson replied. "Everything you say is, I guess, true."

That was too easy. It couldn't be so simple as that. And the priest knew that there was something on the man's mind which he was not saying.

"I got everything figured out," Robinson said enigmatically. "Don't you worry about me." He put down his shovel and poured himself a strong cup of coffee, mixing the condensed milk and the sugar into the thick brew. "No, sir. You just go along and worry about the other men."

Father Hyland went along. There was a man in the carpenter's shack that Greeney had told him about. He sat down and had coffee with him until finally the man began to talk freely.

"Listen," he said. "This whole system is crummy. Something's got to be done."

"Do you know how to do it?"

"No. Nobody does. Here the papers are yelling about parole. What do they know about it?"

There had been fewer complaints recently, the men having things to occupy their time and hands. But here it was again.

"I know that ought to be straightened out. You've got bad publicity—papers—radio—talk. The only ones who get head-lines are the bad eggs. The papers never say anything about the decent men who go straight. That's most of them."

"You bet. But there's more to it. See, I can't get out of this place until I've got a job. Who's going to fix you up? Sure. You can get some jobs. But if I had Al Capone connections, they'd find me a job quick and I'd be out now. But I haven't. I'm a straight guy. I don't know nobody on the outside. So who gets the paroles? Me? Oh no. I've done my minimum—then I get the board. So what? No job. I got five years more. They hadn't ought to do that. They hadn't ought to."

Father Hyland agreed with the man. Sometime—later—here was another task to tackle.

"And say, listen—I got a family. I wrote you a sheet about that."

He remembered. The boy in the reform school—the report on him not good. Crime going on into another generation.

"What did you do for your family when you were out?" he asked.

"Not so good, I guess."

"How will you be to them when you get out?"

"How do I know?"

There it was—this disarming honesty. What could you do against that? The priest rose and went on, to have another cup of coffee with the bricklayer who was always talking about his old sick mother. What had he done for her when he was free? What would he do when he got out? How did he know? And the third cup of coffee with the man Greeney understood so well, whose wife had just run off with somebody else. Another cup with the old man whose children had not written to him in eleven years. Another cup with the lather who had slashed his wife's throat and still bore the ugly mark on his arm where he had tried to do away with himself. And his children? What of them?

So many of them with a dark hatred of their families—blaming them for everything—for not standing by them during trial, for not getting them good lawyers, for neglecting them while they were here, but mostly for writing the terrible letters which came through every day with news of impossible hardships and tragedy at home which these men could do nothing about. Stupid letters. Not vindictive—just stupid. But what heartache they could cause.

He had too much coffee and he was ready to go when Lee Sapis Robinson came over to him.

"I just heard something disturbed me," Lee said.

Secretly, the priest was glad. He did not like Robinson's false placidity.

"What is it?"

"You know Joe that died? What they going to do with him?"

He knew Joe.

"They're going to bury him, Lee," he said.

"Yeah. They gotta do that. But you know Joe's family don't want him. So they tell me they're going to put him in potter's field."

Yes. That was true. "What difference does that make, Lee?"

"That's where Judas was, wasn't it? I don't want to go there."

"Look, Lee. That's just a name. And tomorrow I'm going to bless the grave for Joe. He'll lie in holy ground. And after we have the church he'll be buried from here—with a High Mass and everything. He'll have everything."

"Even if his family don't want him? Even if you haven't any family? You mean even me could get that?"

"Yes, Lee. You could."

"That's worth thinking about. But I'm glad I never had a family. I hate that family stuff. They won't even take you when you're dead."

"I'll tell you more about families, Lee. Next Sunday I'll tell you all about families."

He went down to the office, preparing his prison sermon on families. It couldn't be quite the same as a parish sermon, but as he thought about it, it became clearer and somehow deeper than he would have given in a general congregation. The meaning of the family, what it must mean once they were released—and if they never were to be out what were their obligations, even from here? Surely not perpetual heartache and frustration. Certainly not hatred. Even the birds built nests, cared and fought for their young, taught them how to fly. He would begin with the birds.

There was a letter on his desk when he arrived at the office, distracting him for a while from his sermon preparation. It was from Mother Angela, in response to the one he had written her a few weeks ago.

In its way it was an amusing letter and moving, too, because of its confidence in God. It was a letter which could come only from a nun, a very holy and devoted nun, whose faith in Divine Providence was so unshakable that there could be no question of God's answer to reasonable requests.

He was not to worry about the League for the Separation of Church and State. Just dismiss it and go on building. He was glad that he had anticipated that advice. Her nuns would take care of the League. "My novices behind our walls and your boys behind their walls will be praying together. God wants the church, doesn't He. Well?"

The part about the finances was amusing. "Now I want you to do this," she wrote. "You must make a novena of months to the Infant of Prague. You don't really need the money until then, so there is no use hurrying Him. Then take a blank check. Don't ask for a million, just an honest budget every three months. Fill in that amount on the check; put the date when you expect the Infant to fulfill His promise and have one of your nice repentant forgers sign the name of the Infant. Then put the check under the Infant's crown and on the day the money is due, you will have it."

He laughed out loud. What anyone who did not know would say about this! That is, anyone who did not understand the complete faith, the utter trust, that was symbolized by the naïve gesture.

He would do it. Mother Angela's confidence would supply for his own more sophisticated hesitation. And Carlos Santa Cruz would be delighted to forge the Infant's name for a check—how much was it?—for $14,400 with a better chance of success than he had had last time. Only, if he did it, the Infant must make good. If he didn't, there would be no Church of the Good Thief, and that was unthinkable. He must.

He turned again to his sermon on the family.

2. Bill Martin had gone home. Though even after the guard had slipped the cuffs off him they were never farther from each other than through an open door, he had felt freedom. But what was it like to be outside? He had somehow seen himself going down to a library or up to some musician's studio and asking about courses in music. He hadn't done that at all. All he had done was to visit people he didn't know and couldn't talk to. It would take him a long time to get over it, and sometimes he was sorry he had gone.

Why had they all been so kind to him—his father crying, who had put himself to bed, nursing his chronic ailment so that he would be convincingly sick when the welfare investigator had come; his sister and her children, whom he had never seen before, being so consciously polite; the house, scrubbed and fixed up as he had never remembered it; and being given the best chair, dinner in the dining room, asked what kind of food he liked.

"I just want food," he said, "off a plate." So they had fixed him up things he had never had before.

He had wanted so badly to sit in the kitchen. They never let him do that—not even once. And when he had asked what had happened to the old tinny piano he remembered, he had thought his sister was going to send it out and have one moved in, the way she took on about selling it now that there was nobody to play.

He didn't belong home—outside—any more. These weren't his people. He knew the cons; he could talk to them, but not to these strangers. If only they would let down and not be so careful. If only they would not make him something apart.

The youngsters were the worst, particularly with their mother around all the time to see that they didn't say anything that would remind him of Dannemora or remark on the funny clothes he wore, the way kids do.

The oldest one was thirteen. He was the worst to take, because he didn't have to have reminders. He was careful on his own, treating his uncle with a distant and reserved respect. He was a bright kid, too, you could tell that, and he might have been a lot of fun.

His name was Eddie. He wasn't afraid, exactly, but almost belligerently loyal, so that Bill Martin could tell that all his life he had been defended by this boy who had never seen him. Now that he was here, his reputation was being protected on street corners and in alleys by Eddie's blackened and scratched little knuckles. He knew the boy liked him, but when they were together Eddie had nothing to say to him.

Yes, he was glad when it was time to go back. He was to spend the rest of his life in prison, and he would have to learn how to make something of that life. It was his—not that outside.

He would never forget the farewells—his father's face, his sister clinging to him, the younger children jumping all over him, and Eddie, sitting alone near the window, just sticking out a cold hand toward him, not even looking at him. But then when he was outside and turned back to look down the areaway into the window, he saw Eddie, waving frantically, as if he were all alone, with an expression of adoration in his eyes.

God, that wasn't good! O God, don't let that happen! Eddie must not grow up thinking of him, Bill Martin, as a glamorous figure out of gangland—my uncle who's in prison for life—my uncle who killed a guy. Good God, keep him from that!

Bill Martin made a face at the boy in the window, turned away, and went back where he belonged.

3. Father Hyland's "Family Sermon for Prisoners" was more effective than he had anticipated mainly because he was so deeply moved about something else. In the petitions for the dead he had announced, "Prayers are requested for the repose of the soul of Father Booth, formerly chaplain at Clinton State Prison." He had looked up at the four or five hundred congregated in the auditorium and he had found that the name meant almost nothing.

Five years ago. Less than five years. There must be many here who remembered, but they showed nothing when he made the announcement.

He had toyed with the idea of giving a eulogy of Father Booth, the man who had done so much for them, and to whom once, long ago it seemed, they had been so devoted in the face of this apathy. He gave the sermon which he had prepared, but with more emphasis on the bonds of loyalty, the remembrance of past love, than he would otherwise have done. It may have weakened the analogy with the birds, but he thought he had made a point with that just the same.

Well, the sermon did not really matter. He would have fifty-two Sundays a year to press home that significance of the family. He rather felt that he had been a failure, and he was anxious to get his vestments off after Mass and to be on the road to where Father Booth lay. He was abrupt with Max Bergner. "I can't see you now," he said, "I'm going to Father Booth's funeral. Even if you men don't remember what he did for you, I haven't forgotten. Come around Monday."

He should not have spoken so sharply to poor old Bergner. Hadn't he forgotten something about him? Oh yes—there was that tab asking for an interview. It had been sidetracked somehow. He had never gotten around to it, with the cornerstone and all.

There was always so much to be done. When he got back

from the funeral Monday he would have to see Bergner. No. He couldn't Monday. That was the day the scaffolding was to be removed from around the church and he would have to attend to that. Well, Tuesday then.

Now there was only one thing to think about and to pray for: Father Booth.

4. During the weeks that had passed Max Bergner's sense of abandonment had not lifted, and now there had come this new blow in the knowledge of the death of his first spiritual guide. Father Booth had been no mystic, but he had been sane and sure—the best man, possibly, for starting a soul on the contemplative way.

Max Bergner had not tried until today to see Father Hyland. It was not out of pique, but as a gesture of humility and of abandonment to the will of God that he had not forced his desires upon the priest. Deliberately he had made routine confessions, introducing none of his more abstruse problems.

Things had grown worse for him. His soul now was filled with black doubts and there were moments when he was sure that all his past confessions had been invalid. How could he tell if he had had a sincere purpose of amendment? He was cloistered and had kept himself still more cloistered. Had it been policy, he feared, not love of God? Were he outside, what would he have done? How would God look at that? Then there came the disgust with his whole way of life. He should change, and go out with the other men to help to build a church to God's glory as these better men were doing. He kept thinking that all these years he had been selfish, doing nothing but praying for others when he might have been influencing them for good—actively working for God. The sounds of hammers and chisels from the Church of the Good Thief were torture to him. He liked the silences that came every half-hour when the noises stopped and the tools were being counted by the guards.

His whole life in here had been useless. What could his prayer, his penance amount to?

Yet he held onto this through all desolation. He had been told by Father Hyland and read it in the spiritual books that one should make no radical decision during the Dark Night of the Soul. Then Satan would come as an angel of light, with new and fantastic speculations. You could tell him by the serpent's tail.

Max Bergner, through it all, could perceive the serpent's tail. It was that not only was his own prayer useless, but that all prayer was useless: it was the great temptation to the Active Life.

5. If ever there had been a funeral of a forgotten man, it had been Father Booth's, Ambrose Hyland thought.

Driving back to Dannemora with Joe Hogan, the only guard who had gone to the services, Father Hyland was depressed.

"What did you think of it, Joe?"

"Tough. If he had died a few years ago, the church would have been packed. I don't know what's the matter with people."

Fifteen years, the priest thought—fifteen years of life squandered for criminals, and in return, he was sure, scarcely a prayer. Where the thieves' pastor had lain ironically in state there had been twoscore of the clergy, faithful in death, to chant the Benedictus. But how many of the laity? Father Booth had given up the fellowship of the world to devote his life to strays. And now who, even of them, remembered him?

"Joe Madden was there," Hogan said.

"Yes. That was good. Somebody remembered."

"There should have been more. All the people he helped!"

It had been years, Father Hyland thought, since he himself had faced out the fact of the truth of the parable of the ten lepers. Only one had returned to say thanks. Certainly gratitude was the hardest virtue. He knew the theory. He probably could accept it for himself, but it was hard when you had to apply it for another.

"How could they forget?" Father Hyland asked. "Sure. Sure

they can build a church. There's plenty of excitement and activity about that. They're doing something. They'll be at it today, tearing down the scaffolding—busy as beavers——"

But when they arrived at the site of the church there was no work going on. Joe Hogan went rapidly among the men, questioning, and came back to the priest.

"They're on strike," he said.

"What's the matter?"

"I don't know. They won't talk."

Father Hyland went among them, growling at them. "What's wrong with you? Why aren't you working?" But they did not reply. They were not sullen, exactly—just sitting there unmoving. He went over to the microphone they used for orders in the yard.

"Men," he boomed through it, "come on! Get to work! It's time the scaffolding was down. I thought it would be done before I got home."

There was no response. He could not fancy what had caused this. His abruptness with Bergner might have spread through the yard, but what had he said to him anyway? Nothing very severe, he was sure. Something about Father Booth. Maybe that was it—that he had misjudged them and that he should have talked about the padre instead of about birds and families. It was kind of a silly subject, now that he thought of it, for a congregation of convicts.

He was about to speak again, to apologize to them or to aggravate them into action, when Bud Horne came over.

"If you want to know what's wrong," he said, "just follow me."

Together they climbed a ladder, then to the scaffolding around the tower, still climbing, perilously, it seemed to the priest. His robes were catching in the slivered wood. He was up forty-five feet. He could see over the wall.

"There," Bud Horne pointed.

There was nothing but a nest with three eggs in the crotch of the scaffolding and from a distance a mother bird scolding.

"I don't see anything," he said at last.

"Don't you? See those birds?"

"Why yes," he said.

"Did you mean what you said Sunday?"

"Of course—but——"

"You talked about birds, didn't you?"

"In a way."

"You said they had a right to be born, and that it was wrong to bust up a bird's home. Didn't you?"

That was not the main point, he remembered, but he had said that.

"Yes. I did."

"Well?"

"Well what?"

"Can't you see? If you move the scaffolding you'll bust up their home."

Clinging precariously, the priest looked down. Two hundred men on strike.

"That's what's the matter with the men?"

"What else?"

"And if we save the birds we can move the scaffolding?"

"Yeah. If you meant what you said. If you're no hypocrite."

"All right." He teetered precariously. "We'll move the whole section of scaffolding—not breaking it up—birds and all. O.K.?"

"O.K."

When they had got down Father Hyland went over to the microphone and announced the new operation schedule. It would be heavy work—difficult to move a whole piece of scaffolding. But in a moment they had tackled it, and somehow, though the parent birds screamed at them, they moved scaffolding, nest, and all, without unsetting the eggs.

He had to be serious until he was out of sight. Then he could laugh. Birds indeed! They were all mad—insane. Every one of them. Not a normal reaction in a carload. They were all crazy.

The thought sobered him. That was true. They were not like other men. Their reactions were not the same, and he must not judge them, even their apparent disregard of Father Booth's death. Not like other men—his black sheep. Remember that, keep that in mind all the time. If they were like other men, they would not be here.

And on the hill Bud Horne, watching his descent, said to Cassidy, "He never did understand about us and birds." And Cassidy replied, "Maybe this'll learn him."

6.   Brendon O'Malley could fly again.

That was all that he said to himself, over and over, on his way to England.

"I can fly again!"

They would take him in the R.A.F. In America the national emergency had been declared and he could have gone home but it meant more training. Here, at once, no longer earth-bound, he could fly again. Now.

7.   After Carlos had done an artistic job of forging the check for $14,400 and they had put it under the Infant's crown, and well after the novena of months had started, Tom Riordan pleaded that the statue be brought over to the mental hospital for a few days; and though Cassidy had been a bit bitter about giving up his charge even for a brief time, the Infant of Prague had been installed in a special shrine in the hospital. Now that it was home again, Cassidy should have been happy, but he wasn't. Something was really bothering him, and Father Hyland knew that it had to do with the statue, though what, he could not fancy.

Days went by, and finally Cassidy broke down. "Padre," he said, "I got something awful to tell you. I bet it's the worst thing you ever heard."

The priest had been having interviews that day and some of them had been pretty bad, so if Cassidy's was worse it must be quite something. But Cassidy should be an authority on crime.

"Shoot the works," he said.

"Padre, we're in trouble."

"Who are we?"

"You and I."

"What have *we* done?"

"You know the check the Dago forged for Little Butch? You know, the one we stuck under his hat?"

"Yes?"

"They got the swag."

"What?"

"Sure. They frisked the Infant."

"Who did?"

"The roaches—the guards, I mean. And they got the check off him."

"But what could they do with it?"

"I betcha they got it cashed already. Someone got Little Butch's money."

"But they couldn't have," the priest laughed. "It must have fallen out when we took it over to the other side. Nobody could cash it. You see——"

But how could he explain? Cassidy was deadly serious, facing a major crisis. The priest couldn't very well tell him that the Bambino did not have a checking account. Cassidy was getting purple.

"Listen, Padre, it'll get us all in wrong, snatching Little Butch's check like that. They'll get the Dago for forgery again, and you and me—we'll be excessories, see; and we'll have the whole gang of them down on us. If I was you——"

"I'll start an investigation right away, Cassidy. Don't worry."

"The skunks!"

The investigation uncovered things even more ludicrous than Cassidy's fears. A French attendant at the hospital had found the check, signed as he reported, by one Enfant Prague. This Prague was a very wealthy man, and was either careless, losing checks of nearly $15,000, or else he had intended it as a bribe. Certainly the matter must be looked into.

A report from Albany maintained that the check was authentic. A further probing insisted that it was spurious— clearly a forgery. No one named Prague had a bank account at Plattsburg. Could it be F. Rocque? There were quite a few Rocques about.

It was fairly difficult for Father Hyland to explain the situation to all authorities, but at last he unraveled it, and the Infant's check was returned to its place under the crown.

He wrote all this to Mother Angela, telling her what trouble the Infant had got him into already, and begging her to urge the Lord to remember that two dates had already been set— April 6 for the hearing of the petition of the League for the Separation of Church and State, and August 28 for the dedication of the Church of Saint Dismas. Really, now that the Infant had put him to so much trouble, He must be reminded that He had only the winter left to defend them in the suit and to send them the money.

He was just sealing the letter when Max Bergner knocked at his door and came in.

"May I see you now, Father?" he asked.

"Why certainly. Come in."

"I've tried before—only you were too busy. I won't take long. I just want you to know that for some months I have been most distressed. Sometimes I have had temptations to give up the whole spiritual life. I have even thought it worthless, my father."

"Oh no," the priest said. "You should not have thought that. You should have come to me, told me——"

"But, my father, you were so busy on the church—so many things to think about and do."

"They are not so important as you are. No church is that important, Max."

"Thank you, my father. I have suffered or I would not come."

There were deep hollows under Bergner's eyes—deeper than those already caused by long vigils and superhuman fasting. His face was etched with pain. And all this time, the priest thought, I have been too busy——

"And now, Father, if I am brief, may I talk to you?"

For a moment Father Hyland choked, and could not speak.

Then he put both his hands on the old man's shoulders. "Oh yes, yes, yes," he said. "Now talk to me."

CHAPTER SIX

The months had been all too short. Snow had fallen early and work on the outside of the church had been curtailed, though they were sufficiently well along to do a great many things on the inside. There was no intention of having the decorations complete for the summer, but at least the main structure must be ready for occupancy. The men knew this. Even some of the outside workers would not give up. Bud Horne was working fifteen hours a day.

Part of the time Father Hyland had felt like a prisoner working on his case, there had been so many conferences with Mr. Epstein, for the League's activities had not been curtailed. As yet he had not the slightest idea what he would do with the church should the League succeed.

And he found that in Albany and in Troy the case which Mother Angela was dismissing so lightly had produced an uproar, threatening to spread and to become national. The League was now demanding that the almost-finished building be demolished, removed from the property of the State, and, still more, that there be a discontinuance of the employment and payment of chaplains in all state institutions.

"That's good," Epstein had said. "Let them show their hand. It has passed beyond a straight denominational issue already."

"You mean these people just don't like God."

"That's about the size of it. So no right-thinking man can let them win. It's too dangerous for our country. Think what the precedent would mean."

"I see a little of the danger," the priest said.

"I see a great deal of it. And it's coming. America will be like Russia, if these fellows have their way. They ought to call themselves the League of the Godless."

"That's what they are," the priest said.

"It's the opening wedge. See this last thing. Remove all chaplains of every faith. Get religion totally out of men's lives. That's what it comes down to."

The priest spoke thoughtfully. "I had always imagined the Constitution guaranteed freedom to practice religion—not a license to destroy it."

"It doesn't," Mr. Epstein said. "But if we're not careful we will see the time when it is interpreted that way. One false decision is all that is needed. That's why I'm not fighting this as a Jew and you're not fighting it as a Catholic. We're in this together as God-fearing Americans."

So there were really big issues at stake. He hoped that Mother Angela realized the import of the task she and her nuns had undertaken. As prudently as he could, he alerted the men to the significance of the League and got them praying to the Infant of Prague. He told Max Bergner all about it, and he was sure that with a new cause for zeal in his prayers the old man's own spiritual difficulties were being gradually smoothed away.

Through that winter he himself remained confident on all scores. Though contributions were trickling in, the bills kept mounting higher. But it did not worry him. A good deal of the money he received was sent to him through the bishop, but most of the bills he kept on his own desk as long as his credit would allow. It was not a very businesslike way of acting, but he was a little afraid to have the debt column swell too high on the Episcopal ledger.

There were some substantial donations, and Joe Madden had been as good as his word. He had run a big Christmas party and had had a model of the Church of the Good Thief set up in his restaurant, waylaying customers to explain the project to them, extracting dollars for bricks from them before they could get away. But with all the publicity and all the help there still was not enough.

Then one day in February Father Hyland came into the office jubilantly. "Cassidy," he called, "how much longer does that novena of yours run?"

"Two more months," Cassidy replied.

"Well, it looks as if Little—I mean the Infant—is going to make good before his time runs out. See here! I've got a letter from the cast of *Keep Off the Grass*. They're going to give a benefit performance for us in New York."

Cassidy beamed. "I knew my boy would come through," he said. He patted the Bambino's crown. "You never have to worry about Butch," he said.

The priest was off to New York then for the benefit, allowing himself a couple of days to make arrangements. His first evening in town he dropped in to Joe Madden's for a late supper, having spent the afternoon at the museum, getting ideas for his church, and admiring particularly the magnificent altar which Mme. Latrobe was displaying. It was the original altar which Magellan had transported from Spain to Cebu, where kneeling before it the entire population of the island became Christian.

It was a beautiful and massive piece, just such an altar as one might dream of for the Church of the Good Thief. Father Hyland could scarcely talk of anything else that evening, and it is a good thing that he did so. Ralph Hoy, one of Joe Madden's guests, knew Mme. Latrobe. Yes. She intended to donate the altar to some church, that it might be used again for its original purpose. No. She hadn't made up her mind about where. Why, yes, she could be reached by phone.

Almost before he realized what had happened Father Hyland had an appointment to meet Mme. Latrobe in Washington the following afternoon, and almost an assurance that the Magellan altar would be his.

"Well," he said, sitting down at the table, "that was quick work. I hadn't even contemplated getting an altar yet. What I really was interested in was an organ." He told the story of Bill Martin and his needs, mentioning how hard it was to get a teacher in prison.

"I have had teachers for everything else," he said. "Carpentry, masonry, everything, but nothing for music or sculpture."

"Music? Music teacher? How about Werrenrath?" another man at the table said.

"Werrenrath! Not Reinald Werrenrath? Why, I couldn't afford to get him. He's one of the finest voice teachers in the world."

"Sure," Mr. O'Toole said, "and he's a great fellow. I know him well. He has a country place on a lake not far from you, and if you want me to, I'll ask him about taking your men on. I almost know he'd do it. It's the kind of thing that would appeal to him.

"This is your night, Padre," O'Toole added. He had been looking around the restaurant, and at last his eyes had come to rest on two men who sat under a strange upside-down map of America. "See those lads over there?" he asked. "Well, they're the Brand Brothers—Theatrical Producers. They're just selling out a theater and they've got to do something with the organ. It's a theater organ, but I guess it would do. Kenny here knows them well. Hey—Kenny. Go on over and put the bite on the Brands. The padre here wants their theater organ. That's right. Bring them over here."

Afterward Joe Madden said, "This sure is your night. I think you've got yourself an organ. Hey—wait a minute. See that fellow just coming in? That's Jimmy Durante's agent. He's from that show of yours, *Keep Off the Grass,* that's going to rake you in all that mazula. Might as well press your luck. I'll get him to come over."

As the agent came from the tile-canopied bar he seemed uneasy. "I suppose you got our letter, Father," he said.

"Why, no—except some time ago—telling me about the show."

"Not that one—this last letter. With the bad news."

"I didn't get anything. I just came down to New York."

"Oh? Well, that's too bad. I thought you knew."

"What am I supposed to know?"

"That it's all off. There won't be any show."

He went into a long list of technical reasons why it was impossible, most of which did not seem to make sense to anyone but the show people around. One thing emerged—that there would be no benefit—no money.

"So," Father Hyland said in conclusion, "I have an altar and organ and a music teacher—but I'm not sure yet if I have a church."

He thought of the mounting bills. And as he looked around the restaurant a new significance came to him—stars on the floor, the inverted map—topsy-turvy. He laughed.

2. Carlos was beginning to believe that he had never met an artist before. In the Village he had known many who worked at art, and they were roughly divided into two groups—men like himself, who used art as a means of livelihood, and men who, through failures, assured him and themselves that, while they were the greatest in the world, they would not compromise with current bad taste, and consequently went unrecognized.

But as he watched Cyrus Turner at work on his miniature statues he knew that he was seeing greatness. The statues themselves were crude, often bizarre, but the method of workmanship was somehow honest.

Carlos watched Turner from afar. He knew who Turner was—the man whom Mona loved—but Turner did not know him. While he was working, Turner was self-sufficient, not bothering about anything else, as if he had a world of his own into which he could retreat, and which no one could take from him. He did not care to find Carlos. It was better that way.

For himself, Carlos could not work. Though he was trying to paint, nothing was right. Over and over, partially as a labor of expiation, partially because he was interested, he tried to capture the Good Thief on the cross. But Saint Dismas would not be captured. Then he would daub a big X over the canvas, and for several days brood on his failure. How could you work here? How could you work, when between everything that you had in your mind and every brush stroke on the canvas came a face different from the one you were painting?

He threw himself into the study of the books that Father

Hyland had given him, studying particularly Josephus's history and trying to capture the times and the mood.

He had only one mood.

He was capable of study but not of creation.

It was the routine. Never, never to have time—long hours together—but your whole day broken into by constant reports, searches, shifts from one place to another. It was maddening.

He did not understand how Turner could do it—work for fifteen minutes, then switch off to something else, then return to his sculpture with the same enthusiasm or craftsman's zeal which he had had before. If only Carlos could capture the artist's world!

Yet, had he known it, Cyrus Turner was not satisfied. It was true that for years he had trained himself to an overwhelming concentration so that he could shut out everything when he wanted to; and that was standing him in good stead now. But these little things! Sometimes his fingers would tremble with nervous disgust over the delicate trivials of the tasks which he set himself. Small things, details of this new medium upset him. Once in a while he wanted to throw his soap sculpture into the corner of his cell and be done with it. He would not give up. With terrifying patience he would begin again.

And now he was ready for the second step. It was not the one which Father Hyland had proposed, for he knew that he was not ready for that yet. First he would learn how to make casts and then do some plaster statues; and by that means train himself until he was ready to begin on marble. Someday he would do that! He was not ready yet.

No one except himself knew why he did it—but he knew. He got himself transferred to work in the infirmary and there, caring for the sick, he would do all the less-desired tasks, with the same kind of aloof earnestness with which he had conquered the soap statues. For hours he would mark medical charts. And at night in his cell he would sit, turning his own hands over and over, looking at them, back and front, observing the veins and the knotted muscles until the guards thought he was going mad. He did his daily duties with the same kind of speculative studiousness. He would observe the patients—disease-laden, emaciated, and prison-destroyed.

It was one day late in February when he said to Father Hyland, "I am ready now for the plaster models. I've finished what I set out to do. I'm through at the infirmary."

"But what were you doing there?" No one could understand why he was there in the first place.

"You couldn't—not even you?"

"No. It seemed such a waste of time."

"That's one thing we have plenty of here. It gives us an advantage over other men—outside. No artist has this opportunity. No, I took the time."

"But what did you do with it?"

"I learned anatomy," he said. "Grotesque anatomy. How a twisted soul can twist a body."

He concentrated on his own hands again, turning them over, studying them. Then he looked up.

"I can do gargoyles now," he said; "gargoyles for your tower."

3. Suddenly it was March and there was only intermittent snow; the work on the outside of the church was begun again in earnest. The gargoyles were ready and the trial was approaching, and the novena of months was about to end.

Although inmates were digging up worms for early robins, it was still cold on the hill when the priest came up that morning. It must be slippery on the roof, too, where the slate shingles were being laid. One man kept clambering up to the ridepole and then perilously sliding back.

Each time he did it, Father Hyland caught his breath. If he slipped over the gutters, there would be a sheer drop of seventy-five feet, with nothing between him and the group of workers who watched him from the ground. With the persistence of an insect Bud Horne kept climbing, slipping, catching himself at the last moment, and then climbing again.

The priest joined the group below. One of them said, "We're waiting until he finds out how to do it. Those guys that put up roofs must have some system we don't know."

Bud Horne climbed again, and slipped and caught himself. Then he paused, looking up and down until his glance rested on his feet. Calmly he took off his shoes, tossing them down to the men, and barefooted, without slipping, climbed triumphantly to the ridgepole.

With almost rubrical solemnity the knot of men below removed their shoes, tossing them into a heap from which only a scramble could bring extrication, provided themselves with slate, scaled the ladder, and climbed their barefooted way up the slant of roof. It worked.

They are wonderful, the priest thought. Wonderful. Their feet would ache with the cold before the day was done, but nothing could stop them. They were doing what they wanted. Nothing could stop them. If only, he thought, the League of the Godless could see them now.

At the base of the tower there was a loud argument going on. Cassidy was the leader of the opposition.

"You're crazy," he was saying. "At least Little Butch is good-lookin'. But you're not going to put these things up on no church. Will you look at them, will you?"

They certainly were hideous. The priest smiled, seeing their frightfulness, an epitome of all the horrors of sick convicts in their every scowl.

"The padre says they're going up and they're going up," Greeney yelled back, his blood rising.

"Says you?"

"Yeah—says I."

"Aw, what does it matter?" Bill Martin cut in. "They're going to be up so high nobody can see 'em anyhow."

"It don't matter if nobody sees 'em," Cassidy shouted. "They're a disgrace to the church."

There's the complete medieval attitude, Father Hyland

thought as he approached rapidly—men not caring whether details could be seen or not, as long as they were part of the cathedral. And Cassidy, of all men, had captured it.

"Hey," Cassidy called when he saw the priest coming, "what the—I mean—what are these—dafool things, anyhow?"

The priest explained about gargoyles, but he was unconvincing until he thought of a new way to put it. "Just let's say they're evil—they're the wickedest things in the world, made to frighten the evil spirits back to hell."

Cassidy's puzzlement disappeared and a look of great comprehension dawned. "I get it!" he shouted. "And they sure look it. The wickedest things in the world. You bet." He rubbed his hands together. "O.K., men, hoist 'em up."

With one gargoyle hanging treacherously in mid-air Cassidy stopped the work. "Say, Padre, did you say the wickedest things in the world?"

"I did."

"And they're supposed to be damned, aren't they? Everything else blessed and these things damned?"

"That's right."

"Well, you do the blessing—but we're the guys for the damning. And I got them named."

So through the rest of that morning, with each haul, as the evil figures jerked upward to the top of the tower, Father Hyland could hear the men grunting as they pulled at the ropes, "Damn you, Adolf! Damn you, Tojo! Damn you, Benito!"

But looking at the figures Father Hyland had his own name for them. "The League for the Separation of God and Man," he called them.

4. Then it came. The Case, April 16, 1940. A Summary of the Findings of Justice Russell:

The first cause of action alleges that the defendants, Commissioner of Correction of New York State and members of the Commission of Correction of the State have violated certain provisions of the Constitution of the State of New York and the Correction Law of the State of New York, in permitting to be constructed upon State property at Clinton Prison a chapel or building to be known as the "Church of Saint Dismas, the Good Thief."

In the second cause of action it appears that said church is being constructed by prison labor volunteered for that purpose and that funds and materials are being supplied through gifts.

The third cause of action alleges in substance that the statutes of the State are unconstitutional which permit the employment of Chaplains at State Correction Institutions for the purpose of religious observances for inmates pursuant to the provisions of the Correction Law, namely, Sections 9, 18, and 274.

The petitioners ask that the structure at Clinton Prison be demolished and that said building be removed from the property of the State for an order directing the cessation and discontinuance of the employment and payment of said Chaplain in said Institution.

The questions of law arising out of the allegations of the petitioners narrow down to one important question, namely: Is it constitutional for the State of New York to furnish facilities for religious worship and instruction to the inmates of State Institutions where said Institutions have been erected by gifts of funds or materials on State property? The plaintiffs contend that the erection of any chapel by prison labor on State property even though a gift is in violation of Art. 7, Section 8, of the State Constitution, which in substance forbids the use of State funds for anything but State purposes. The State contends that when erected on prison or reformatory property they become the property of the State and that they are used for State purposes in providing the prisoners with adequate facilities for the free exercise of their religious belief and worship which is guaranteed to "all mankind," by Art. I. Section 3, of the State Constitution, and is in accord with legislative provisions pursuant to Sections 610 and 18 Subd. 2 of the Correction Law.

It is therefore mainly upon these sections that the conflict of opinion between the plaintiffs and the State arises. It might be well to state at this time the cause or source which permitted, in the discretion of the Commission of Correction, the erection of these chapels. It appears in the Brief on behalf of Amici Curiae that in

1937 Clinton Prison was overcrowded. Many of the mental cases transferred to Dannemora State Hospital were caused by continuous idleness in confinement. The prison officials were helpless to provide jobs or courses in building trades. In order to meet this situation they decided "upon an educational and welfare project for the erection side by side of three buildings to be used as the Protestant, Hebrew, and Catholic Churches." For this project the respective Chaplains had to seek private resources for the cost of construction. The Catholic Chaplain was the first to obtain the necessary resources for that project. It, therefore, cannot be said that the prison officials have discriminated in favor of any particular denomination.

The prisoner is confined within the grounds of the prison. His civic liberty has been taken away. To deprive him because of such confinement of the right to worship would be to deprive him not only of the very right the Constitution of the State grants him, but also of one of the most essential factors in his rehabilitation. The very purpose of his imprisonment is not only to punish him for the crime he committed but to prepare him vocationally, physically, mentally, and spiritually for return to society. The prisoner does not need to worship if he so desires, but if he does, he should not be denied that privilege. That is the intent of the Constitution. To many confined, the deprivation of spiritual solace would be greater than that of the other necessities which they receive. The relationship of religious faith to the very foundation of our Government and the welfare of society should not be severed.

The Courts have universally concurred in the doctrine that the stability of our government rests upon the basis of a religious belief in God. By allowing the inmates of its institutions the freedom of worship and supplying them with the adequate facilities for that purpose, the State is permitting the spirit of the Constitution to be fulfilled.

I am therefore of the opinion that neither constitutional nor statutory provisions are violated by the building of the aforesaid church on State property where such a church is not built by funds of the State. The permission to build by the State is in keeping with the freedom of worship as expressed in the Constitution.

5.   Father Hyland returned from the trial jubilant; and he had another cause for jubilation. He called Cassidy into the office.

"When does your novena end?" he asked.

"Tomorrow. Gee, Padre, I'm glad you won the case. That's swell. But I can't get over Little Butch letting you down. He should have got you the money."

Then the chaplain could not wait, as he had planned, until the next day, but he had to show Cassidy now. It had all happened in the last week, the publicity given to the trial, stirring up the interest that was needed.

"Look," he said. "Bring me in that check the Infant of Prague made out. Then look at these books!"

There was no large bequest among them—twenty-five cents from a scrubwoman; contributions here and there from Joe Madden's customers; ten dollars from an anonymous parolee; many dollars from grateful families of prisoners who had been helped; and hundreds from the vast, unknown public who had come to believe in the Church of the Good Thief.

The check from the Infant's crown was for $14,400; on the back side of the ledger Cassidy read $14,722.20.

"Butch!" Cassidy cried. "Listen, kid, all the time I didn't believe it. I talked big, but honest I didn't think you had it in you."

Then he turned to Father Hyland. "Can I use the seventy-two twenty?"

"I suppose so. What do you want it for?"

"For one swell Joe. I want it for Little Butch!" Then he looked at the statue. "If it's up to me, kid," he said, "you'll get the best spot in the church."

6.   "I can't do it, Padre." Carlos threw down his brush in disgust. "Look—you see that daub? It's rotten. That isn't Saint Dismas—or anything human. I'm just no good."

Setting up an easel secretly in the tower, where the north light was strong, Father Hyland saw what Carlos meant, and quietly agreed with him. It would never do, and they did need a painting of Saint Dismas to hang over the high altar, between the rich onyx columns of the canopy. He had thought that Carlos would be just the man. The altar needed something barbaric and splendid—but something more like Saint Dismas than like a stylized and crucified Saint Aloysius, which Carlos had painted, complete with halo.

"Can't you let yourself go?" the priest asked.

"In here?"

"Forget that it's a holy picture. Put some life in it."

"How can I? What life is there in me?"

"Oh, hang the self-pity and paint!" Maybe, he thought, if he could make Carlos angry something might happen.

"Who do you think I am—a great artist like Cyrus Turner?"

"No. I think you're a no-good counterfeiter from the Village. That's what that chrome is—it's counterfeit. It's a fake."

"What do you expect?"

"Something honest for a change."

"If I could work from a model——"

"That's what got you into trouble the first time, wasn t it— working from models? And not good enough——" He stopped short. He saw a new gleam in Carlos's eye. "Say," he said, "how about that? Why not get a model? You know what you need?"

"Yes. I know. There is such a man."

"You need to do the hardest thing in the world, Carlos. You've got to take a thug and make him into a saint."

"That's right. He's got to be mean, and then—suddenly, like that—a saint. Yes."

"No wonder it was hard. It *is* hard!"

"There must be someone in here who looks like that!"

"You certainly have plenty of thugs. I'll ask one of my men if he knows anybody who'll do." Father Hyland saw Dominic below, scowling at Cassidy.

"Dominic!" he called out.

"Hey, Pops!"

Carlos Santa Cruz grasped the priest's arm. "Oh yes," he cried. "Yes! That's it!"

"What is?"

"My man—my Saint Dismas!"

"But I was only going to ask him to find someone for us."

"Did you see it? He looked ugly. Then you called him, and he looked up, and he saw you, and he was—he was beautiful!"

Father Hyland had never considered Dominic exactly beautiful, but seeing him with Carlos's eyes was different. For one moment Dominic had been beautiful.

"Dominic," he said, "do you want to be Saint Dismas?"

"What gives?"

"I want you to pose for me, on a cross—like Saint Dismas," Carlos said.

"Aw—go on."

"He's serious," the chaplain explained. "We want you to hang over the high altar—your picture, I mean."

"What I gotta do?"

"Look," Carlos instructed him, "you will stand on a keg—let us tie you to a cross like this—and then I will paint you—immortally. Have you got muscles?"

For answer Dominic stripped off his shirt. Thank God, he had never let himself get soft. His muscles rippled like a boxer's.

"You like 'em?"

"Magnificent. Now get up there. Try hard. Look pained— look pained——"

But for days, while Dominic posed and Carlos painted feverishly, nothing went right. No sooner would Dominic get into position than a new and utterly false cherubic smile engulfed him. He knew he was a saint.

"All the time," Carlos said, "he tries to look pretty."

"Yes," Father Hyland said, "it is pretty awful. Some photographer once must have told him to smile. He's very obedient."

"What can we do?"

"Try once more."

Together they tied Dominic to the cross and stood him on his keg, and Dominic beamed upon them.

"No! No!" the priest commanded. "Don't do that!"

"But I'm supposed to be a saint!"

"Forget it. Just be Dominic."

"Look pained," Carlos called. Dominic did. It was far worse.

"Stop looking like anything," Father Hyland advised. The expression now was completely moronic.

"I give up." Carlos laid down his brush.

"What's the matter? Don't you like my muscles?"

"It isn't your muscles," Father Hyland told him; "it's your face!"

"Aw—have a heart. I stand here all day for you, then you don't like me. So what do I do?"

"Nothing," the priest said. "Just nothing."

Quite deliberately, slowly, he went over and kicked the keg out from under Dominic. For a moment there was silence, then Carlos seized his brush and began. Dominic cried, "Hey! I'm dying! Put the keg back! I'm dying!" And he hung there by the ropes, suspended on the cross.

"Hurry up, Carlos," the priest said. "Better not kill him."

"Aw! Gimme back the keg!"

Carlos worked savagely. "I got it," he said. "Yes, I got it." He painted faster. "Any time you can put the keg back. Let him down. Did you see—that first moment?"

And so the painting was made, and so it hangs now over the main altar of the Church of the Good Thief—the perfect Dismas. There is no doubt but that a criminal is converted suddenly upon the cross. His head is turned up toward a Voice; his muscles are contorted, but above all he has heard something that has penetrated his agony—something he could not have believed. There is no question at all but that Dismas at that moment listened incredulously to One saying, "This day thou shalt be with me in Paradise."

And the great authenticity of the painting was achieved by a simple means—the agony, the amazement, the sudden change, the utter reality. Very simply, when Father Hyland kicked the keg out from under Dominic, Dominic forgot to pose. For a moment he was a criminal who relapsed unto childlike innocence, pained, but still half-pleased. It was all very simple. Dominic, like the Good Thief, looked surprised.

CHAPTER SEVEN

It was the morning of August 28, 1941, and Ambrose Hyland was already tired. He stood now at the entrance of his own enclosure, waiting for the guard to open the gate. The great meaningless wall that had not yet been removed cut off the church enclosure from the Big Yard. Sometime soon, he thought, that must be adjusted so that the men could have easy access to the church. But it was just as well today, while the dedication ceremonies were going on, to have this separation.

Looking up on his side of the wall, he saw that the men had done their best to cover the still remaining piles of debris with tarpaulin; there was much work still to be done—the grounds, the decorations, some sculpturing, but the church stood, the building itself, complete. And though its lines were magnificent it still looked raw, somehow, as all buildings did before occupancy. But someday that would be remedied. Thousands of feet would come up these stairs. They would begin today. This is what he had lived for so many years. But was it?

A voice was calling to him from the new hospital wing on his right.

"Nice morning, Padre! How are you? How's things?"

He looked up to see the black face of Lee Sapis Robinson grinning down at him.

"Just fine," he shouted back. "What are you doing in there?"

"I'm sick. Just plain old sick."

"What've you got?"

"They can't figure. I got them fooled, I guess." The Negro broke into the low, rumbling chortle that was a delight to hear.

"I guess you won't die this time," the priest said, picking up his two black bags as he saw the guard coming to let him through the gate.

"I might. I just guess I might," Robinson predicted, his voice still full of glee.

"You'd better not! You get out of there and come up to the dedication today."

Lee Robinson's voice was growing more distant as the priest climbed up the hill. "Guess they won't let me. But I'll be listenin'. I'll be hearin' everything where I am."

The priest lifted one of his bags in a kind of salute and then stopped. Halfway down the steep hill to the right he saw a couple of old boards left carelessly. He must have Cassidy pick these up before the bishop arrived. Everything must look as finished as possible.

He was glad to stop for a moment. Already, though it was early morning, it was growing hot. He hoped it would not be uncomfortably so, but it was like the first day he had come here. No, not quite. He looked up at the church, solid, standing there. Not quite. There had been some changes, he thanked God. A beginning. That was all, though.

When he reached the church he found Joe Hogan waiting for him. It annoyed him a little because he had expected to be alone for his Mass this morning. Later, when the bishop and all the guests came, it would turn into their day. But now he had hoped he could have his moment, saying what would really be the first Mass in the Church of the Good Thief. That was all he had asked for himself. But the presence of a guard meant that some of the church crew must be here already.

"The boys beat me, did they?" he asked the guard.

"Only one, Father."

"Oh. I see." He knew of course who it would be and was not surprised, therefore, when he found a solitary gray figure kneeling there in front of the great altar. It was Max Bergner. That was all right.

Together, without words, Max and he went into the sacristy and Bergner took prison-made vestments from the priest's bags, laying them out, careful as any nun, and with the same precision, helping the priest vest. Together they went out, celebrant and acolyte, to the single man in the congregation, to Joe Hogan and to the first Mass in the Church of the Good Thief.

That Mass and the moments afterward with Max Bergner,

Father Hyland was to remember as the high spots of the day. Later there were so many distractions and so many things that he could not explain to the people who came. How could they understand that, with the church complete, this was not the conclusion and the triumphant climax of his plans? But Max Bergner could understand. Almost alone he could enter into the priest's feelings when he pointed out what still remained to be done and to understand the significance of the things already accomplished. He had been here. He knew.

"The tile floor looks nice, doesn't it?"

"It is good." Max smiled softly.

Not only the tiled floor was in their thinking now, but also the man who had made it. He had been a two-time loser with forty years for armed robbery. They had picked him out to prepare the acids for the tiles because he knew so much about "soup"—the mixing of explosives for the blowing up of safes. And this old robber had insisted on doing all the work himself, though the acids burned into his flesh and he had been hospitalized several times. And even today he would come here, looking proudly at his floor, and hiding his bandaged hands, until the time came for him to fold them at the altar rail when he received his first Holy Communion.

"Look over there, Max," the priest said, pointing to the far right wall. "We'll have a shrine of Saint Dismas and a statue in it better than the one over the front door. Saint Dismas looking down from the cross."

"Cyrus Turner." Max nodded. He had seen Turner's work on the gargoyles and it had been hideous, but if the good father believed that Cyrus Turner would someday carve a beautiful thing, he would be right. Already, Max knew, an ugliness in the mind of Cyrus Turner had gone out of him and now there was room for the beautiful thing in the mind that an artist could make into a beautiful thing outside.

"I haven't told anybody else this, Max," the priest confided. "You see, just the other day Turner did a statue of the Sacred Heart. It was pretty bad, Max."

The priest smiled ruefully, thinking of the monstrosity. The hands, particularly. Turner had looked down at his own great hands, then at the hands of the statue.

"It looks as if he had boxing gloves on," he said.

Father Hyland had to laugh. "That's probably very significant, Cy. Maybe you were thinking that even the Lord would need boxing gloves in this place. But you're wrong. It's only His ministers who need them."

"No," Turner replied, "I was thinking of something else. I was getting my own hands out of my mind." He took up a mallet to destroy the statue.

"Don't do that," the priest commanded. "I'm going to set this statue up."

"You can't have that thing in the church!"

"No. I can't even have it outside in the garden. You've got to do a Madonna and some children praying for the shrine. But I can set it up down at my place on the lake, and years from now I'm going to say, 'That's the first Cyrus Turner. You wouldn't think he ever did things as bad as that, would you?'"

"You believe in me that much?"

"You will do beautiful things."

Now Max Bergner echoed his thoughts. "He will make beautiful things," he said, and then he added, "And Carlos?"

The priest turned and pointed to the large mural over the Magellan altar. "That will always be Carlos," he said.

"It is good. And the altar is good."

Again they were thinking of the same thing—the sleight-of-hand artist who had done his legitimate work on the vaudeville stage using an amazing series of boxes with secret compartments, assembling them, making them large or small at the touch of his hand. But who had shifted his talents into rather more dubious games of three-card monte, and had been caught one day. He had come offering to defray the expenses of the church by doing card tricks, but had been persuaded instead to work on the Magellan altar which Mme. Latrobe had sent.

It was a difficult and fine task. The pieces of stone had to be assembled; the great but broken carvings around the sides put into place as accurately as a jigsaw puzzle. Now it was done— a majestic piece standing ready for the High Mass. The morning sun shone in clear white rays through the plain windows.

That was another thing. "See those windows, Max? Someday we will have our own stained glass in them. We'll make it ourselves, Max."

"There are fourteen windows—like the Stations of the Cross."

"Good man," Father Hyland said. "You saw through it. We're putting the Stations into the windows."

"I wonder why no other church ever thought of that."

"No other church could do it, but we can because there will always be a daytime church, and you can only see stained glass in the daytime. Nobody will ever come here at night."

"Except you, my father."

"Except me, Max, and I'll always see them."

They had turned now for a last look at the baptistry made by a pickpocket turned cabinetmaker. It was in order after yesterday. Seventy-four men had been baptized there. There should have been seventy-five if Lee Sapis Robinson had not resisted.

This was his own moment, Father Hyland reflected, and he was glad that Max Bergner was here to share it with him. For the first time he realized what a close companionshp he had had with the old man—a silent companionship, too silent sometimes, he remembered.

"Max," he said, "after this is over I want a long talk with you. Not now, because——" He waved down into the valley where the church crew was already waiting for Joe Hogan to let them into the compound.

"It would be good, my father," Max said. "Only it will not be."

"Why, Max?"

"Because in two days I go. I did not tell you. You have had enough to think about. Now they know I am harmless and I can go."

"You mean you're getting out?"

"Yes. I have received executive clemency. No one is afraid of me and it is good."

"It's good for you, Max. I'm glad." He was glad for the old man, but for himself——

"Yes. I am no longer afraid even of myself. So now I can go. That is why I wanted to serve your Mass today. You have done much for me."

The priest felt ashamed, thinking how much more he could have done and had not had time to do. But now with the church built he could have time. He could do things for the men—make them more like Max.

"I haven't done anything, Max. But you've done a lot for me. You don't know it, but you see those men coming up there? One day you made me realize what it was all about—not just building a church—but building a church so that it may help the men. That's the big job. You've made me see that."

"I am glad."

"What will you do, Max?"

"If I had a chance I would join a religious order, but who would take me, my father? There should be a religious order for men like me—and like them."

"Yes. Once they have learned what we teach them here, there should be some place for them to go, and not back to the old gangs. But there isn't."

He thought then that there might be a place for Max, who was already a contemplative. Some penitential brotherhood might take him in. But for those others, who needed an active life as well as a life of prayer, who had learned the meaning of hard work for God—where could he send them?

Max answered his thoughts. "You have built this church, my father. You can do the other thing too."

"I know it is more important; I know it is."

And all through the preparations for the Pontifical Mass and through the Mass itself Father Hyland was filled with the thought, hearing it in the glowing words of the bishop, seeing it as His Excellency spoke that day to the two thousand men who had filled the church and overflowed into the great spaces where the monastery gardens would be. He kept seeing them all, not in the blurred outlines of their regimentation, but as individuals, each with his own problem, each one to be rehabilitated, treated according to his own need. That was the meaning of the church, the things to come.

Even at the lunch which followed, while he was gracious enough to the bishop and the guests, his mother had to speak to him.

"What are you thinking about, Ambrose?"

"The men," he said. "Individuals."

"Well, there's one individual I wish you'd think more about and that's the bishop. He's enough individual for one day."

So he thought about the bishop, and he thought about each of the distinguished guests who came during the afternoon—the hundreds for whom the prison gates would be opened for the first and only time—who were allowed to climb up the hill to attend solemn benediction at the new church.

But then, just before benediction, he had a distraction. As he was slipping into his dalmatic and settling its gold more squarely on his shoulders, Greeney, resplendent in his cassock and benediction surplice, came over to him.

"Pops," he whispered, "they just telephoned up from the hospital. They want you soon as you can come. I told them you wouldn't, but they said soon as you could."

"What was it?"

"A guy down there, named Lee Sapis Robinson, wants you to come quick."

"I will," he said. "I will."

Around him the great pageantry of that afternoon went on —the bishop in his purple, the visitors, men and women, all of them the great of the world; the background of the vested choir and the men in gray; the true magnificence of the new church now formally dedicated; and the words, the words of praise for what he had accomplished against such great obstacles, all meaningless as one after one he looked at his men.

As if a spotlight played upon them individually he saw

them. He knew so many of them now—hundreds, he realized
—better than any other man would ever know them. Their
faces were shining in the afternoon sunlight. They were looking at the church—their church, which they had built themselves, the first ever within prison walls. It was theirs. And it
would go on. And their lives would go on, but the church was
a means, not an end. They were the purpose of it.

And like an undersong through the magnificence of that
afternoon there kept coming to him, "One man wants you.
Lee Sapis Robinson is waiting."

He was not brusque. He could not hurry these people away.
They, too, had been individuals, fighting for him, supporting
him in this great and at last triumphant cause. It was their
church which they would never see again. He knew that.

But so many of them, so many of the world at large, would
think that the talk was done. He still wanted to shout to them
that it was only the beginning. He still had the monastery
garden to construct, so that those who could not feel at home
in his church might have a place to pray. There was still a
paradise to make within prison walls.

And there were other things—Greeney to get justice; Bud
Horne to lose his bitterness; Bill Martin to find a life within a
lifetime sentence; Cassidy to go home to his own bambinos;
and poor Dominic—to get something, something——

Yet he was conscious of a slight twinge of disappointment
after the ceremonies were over, and instead of talking about
the church the enthusiasm was mainly about the music.

Werrenrath had come over, big and hearty. "You want me
to teach this boy? I will do more—I will come and sing in
your choir. Of course I will teach him. The music was splendid—wonderful. I will do anything. But once, at least, I wish
you would let me sing in your choir."

Others had come too. They mentioned the beauty of the
church, and it was beautiful now that people had been in it,
its one slender spire rising above the walls; its magnificent
stone losing its heaviness in a clime of light; its great doorway,
a wide gate that would never be closed. But though the guests

were appreciative they had been lifted upon a wave of sound, and, for the most part, they could talk only about the music.

It was a disappointment until he saw Bill Martin. Then he knew. One man. Nothing can be done for a crowd. This was Bill Martin's day. Hereafter in the memory of this a lifetime would not have been spent in vain.

It was Cassidy's Bambino. It was Turner's gargoyle. It was the tiles and the altar and the baptistry. It was Dismas over the altar where Carlos's mural hung with the picture of Dominic. It was Mother Angela in her cloister. It was Mrs. Hyland. It was Joe Hogan. It was Max Bergner. It was the hope for Bud Horne. It was the thousand men yet to come and one among them. It was Greeney saying, "Pops." And it was Lee Sapis Robinson.

2.   In the hospital that morning Lee Sapis Robinson heard the music. It came drifting down from the hill, and it was most beautiful. All around him the ward grew quiet; and in the August sunshine there were little angels dancing on the window sill.

Sometime he knew that he would have a sign, and this was it. He had heard the music of the organ and the singing, like something far away, calling to him, and there was a beauty about him as there had never been before. There was a better land far, far away. Only not so far. He could make it come nearer. He wanted that land.

So Lee Sapis Robinson did what he had had in his mind to do for a long time.

3.   It was already dusk when Father Hyland at last reached the new infirmary. He had called up to say that he was coming, and a white-coated orderly was waiting for him on the third floor.

"It's Robinson," he said. "Tried to bump himself off."

The priest's hand went involuntarily to the pyx and the Blessed Sacrament which he had brought. The lines deepened around his tired mouth. "Oh," he said. It was all he could say now.

"He ain't dead yet. They cut him open. But he hasn't got a chance. Swallowed some bedspring filings in a piece of sock."

"Suicide," the priest said. "I see." He had so hoped—— But somewhere he had failed. What could he do now? He had built the church, yes, but it was meaningless if he were to fail with individuals like this. There was nothing he could do.

Outside, as if in mockery, came the voices of the choir singing their last notes as, with lighted candles, they descended the hill. It had been their triumph, not God's!

And then, raucously from above him, he heard other voices, jeering voices shouting from the roof of the hospital at the sacred procession. Under the beauty sounded the ugliness. Loudly from above came the jeers of their dying inmates, shouting "Onward, Christian Soldiers!"

Over the mingled sounds Father Hyland shouted. "Where is he? Where is Robinson?" He was not dead, was he? He could still try.

"Ward 3B. There isn't a chance, Padre. He's a no-good nigger."

Suicide. Done for himself. Too late.

If he had destroyed himself, what could a priest do?

He could go to him.

"I'll see him anyway," he said.

"What good'll it do? He's bumped himself off."

Fortunately, then, a gruff voice broke in. It was the doctor in charge. "Sure it's suicide," he said, "if you want to put a name on it. And I suppose men of your cloth will have nothing to do with him."

"I just said I was going to see him!"

"Yes. You'll see him all right. And I suppose you'll judge him. Listen here, Padre. We brought this man in here for observation. We knew he was going stir-crazy, see? Well, he was. He got ahead of us—swallowed some filings in a bit of sock. We cut him open—tried to save him. That's more than you'd do."

Around them the air was filled with sound—the choir, singing at the top of their lungs, trying to drown the inmates crying, "Onward, Christian Soldiers." It was a turmoil, but had given him hope. If Lee Robinson had not been right in the head——

"Show me where he is. I'm going to him."

When he had reached the bedside and touched the dark brow, Lee Sapis Robinson opened his eyes and looked at him.

"I'm glad you came, Padre. I'm glad you came. I've been waiting."

"I'm here, Lee," was all he could say.

"Look, Padre, I heard that music. It came down over me like out of heaven. They kept telling me it was better on the other side. All my life they told me. So I decided I better find out. I've never been no place but jail all my life. Don't remember much of anything else, 'cept for a few days, maybe in and out. Never did think much of this life."

There were cries from the roof. "What's that, Padre?"

"Nothing," the priest said. "Just somebody yelling his head off that will be yelling for me in a few days. That's all."

"It's like hell and heaven. You wouldn't let me go to hell, will you Father?"

"No, Lee. Not if you don't want to." Then he asked the question that he had to ask, the only question: "Didn't you ever think it was wrong to do what you did? You had so many months to think."

"Just once or twice. Just when you told it was wrong in your class and I stopped coming, remember? You said only God had a right over life. Guess I got worried then. But I thought God would think special about me. So I just kept on filin'. An' I didn't come back to hear any more until I heard that singing today. Do you think God will think special of me?"

The priest wanted to say that he was sure that God would, but he could not condone this. What Lee had done was wrong, and there was to be no compromise with that. Then he found the way.

"Lee," he said, "I don't know what God thinks. I only know

what you did was bad. And you'll be sorry for it if it was bad, won't you, Lee?"

"I'm sorry for all the bad things I done. Every one of them. And if you say I should be sorry for this, I'll try—but I'll still feel glad I'm going to see Jehovah."

"Even if He didn't want to see you yet—this way?"

"Then I'll be sorry for Him—but I can't claim I'm sorry for myself."

"O Lord, Lord," the priest prayed, "what more can you ask? This thing he says may not make sense, but it sounds like love and faith and hope—and it's all wrong. Yet what chance has he had?"

"Will you baptize me now, Padre?"

There was no time for delicate moral problems. Perhaps the grace of God could do what he could not do. There were a few moments left for instruction, and he gave them, and then he brought out the baptismal water which he carried, and he baptized Dismas Lee Sapis Robinson.

Dismas Robinson said to him, "Now I want to receive the Lord Jesus." And then he said, "I guess you was right, Father. I shouldn't have hastened my going there. I never thought of it this way. I guess I was wrong—but I want my Lord Jesus."

So the seventy-fifth convert received his first Communion that night, and as Ambrose Hyland went toward the forbidding gates, the white moon was shining amid a silence and a peace, while from many a square-barred window a prisoner looked up the hill to a cross that surmounted the Church of the Good Thief, where now the Lord Jesus lived.

And Lee Sapis Robinson, called Dismas, was sorry for what he did, for hastening the coming, and went that night fresh from baptism into the benign judgment of God.

4. Two days later, while the choir was singing its first requiem in the new church, Max Bergner was waiting in the administration building for his release. Over the loud-speaker he could hear the voices, singing as they had never sung before, and now he could translate their words.

"Libera nos, Domine."

"Free us, O Lord."

Both of them, he and the new soul, would be free.

He heard the call, and with the obedience of many years followed the guard.

The street lay before him. Across the way there was a bus waiting. Over there was a sign, "Ting's Tavern." On the village street were people. He crossed the street, clutching the bus ticket in his hand.

"Libera nos, Domine."

5.   In England, Brendon O'Malley was in the air. He was free. His body was not crippled any more. He was fighting for the certain cause of freedom against a known oppressor. And he was in love.

The gold cloud was below him.

In his rich baritone, above the noise of the motor, he sang as he had not sung in years, some old remembered words— "Free us, O Lord . . ."

BOOK THREE: OUT OF THE NIGHT

CHAPTER ONE

"Say, Padre, wait a minute," Joe Hogan shouted.

Father Hyland stopped at the wire gate that closed off his section of the hill, until a guard came to open the lock for him. Beyond the still-remaining wall that shut off the church sector from the Big Yard, skiers swooped over ledges, landing perilously amid skaters. Far below, the wartime factory was letting one shift out, and another shift waited to go in. But on his own hilltop, the priest knew, was the greatest activity of all.

"Boy, what a day," Hogan said, stamping the heavy snow from his boots. "Where are you off to?"

"I'm going to look in at my schools. Want to come?"

"You bet."

The guard let them past the gate and with lowered heads they thrust their way through the wind.

"I don't like that," the priest panted.

"What?"

"That gate. And the wall——" He paused for breath and pointed at the great bastions on his left, still surmounted with abandoned turrets. "All it does is cut the Big Yard off from us —makes it harder for men to get to church. They have to run a gantlet every time." Inmates were staring at them, even now, from their own enclosure. "That's no good. Got to get it down."

"Want me to get you a pick? You pulled one wall down already. You don't know when you're through."

"Through?" Father Hyland started the climb again. "We— haven't—even—begun."

He was disturbed that Hogan should say that. People seemed to think that once the church was erected, the task was finished. It was obvious, wasn't it, that it was only beginning?

What was the use of a church if it was not to be the means of rehabilitation? Construction alone was not the cure for prison fatigue. At best it was a temporary cessation of abuses. Three shifts of war work kept the hitherto-blackened windows blazing all night; but ultimately the war work would stop. The trouble with a building program was that eventually everything would be built. Then what? Back to the old idle companies? He vowed that that must never happen.

"Come on," he called back. "I'll show you something."

The church itself, when they reached the vestibule, was bright with the strange brightness that comes with the falling of snow, and it looked large and chilly. There was no one in it.

"See? That's what I mean. The idea was to have a place men could come to. But what's been done? I admit they can't tear down a wall as fast as I'd like them to and open us up to the Big Yard, but they needn't fence us in like this."

"I guess it does make it hard."

"Hard? Impossible. The men have to go through four gates to get up here. They have to wait for four guards to unlock them. Then they have to pass muster of all those eyes on them. Hard?" he repeated. "It's heroic."

"Who's responsible?"

Father Hyland grinned. "You'd better not ask. I'll only say this—that that certainly wasn't Warden Murphy's intention, and it certainly wasn't Warden Snyder's. *Comprenez?*"

Joe Hogan grunted. After all, he was a guard. And there had been a lot of talk recently about the chaplain's being misunderstood by some of the prison administrators. Warden Murphy had understood the priest's position, that he had to be pro-con, and Warden Snyder did too. But would the new men who followed?

"Come along," the chaplain beckoned him on. "This isn't what we came to see."

Together they went down the narrow stairs beneath the tower. There certainly was enough activity in the basement. The entire place was partitioned off and each room was a separate workshop.

In the first they found men busy with hand-wrought iron, making great conical-topped lamps and railings and *prie-dieus,* strong, yet delicate. Their civilian instructors had long since gone and now a new crew was being trained by inmate craftsmen.

"Hi, Pops!" A little, shriveled Frenchman looked up at him. "How you like this, what?" He pointed to an intricately wrought candelabrum, scrolled and entwined with sheaves and grapes, each detail beaten, hammered with infinite intrepidity.

The priest spoke in rapid French, and the man beamed, while Joe Hogan stared at the work in amazement.

When they had gone out he asked, "What's he in for?"

"Him? I don't know. I don't ask. All I know is that he's a 'reformed character.' He told me that. He's got a long term, can't read or write, comes from the backwoods. We started him off with the church benches but he transferred here when the fine woodcraft began. He knew about wood so he was afraid of it. But he doesn't know anything about iron."

"He doesn't?"

"Well—he didn't, then. But he does now, doesn't he?"

"I'll say. Are they all like that?"

"Pretty much." The priest opencd the door of the woodcraft cubicle. "This is what Jacques was afraid of." Men here were putting the finishing touches on the bishop's throne. It was of green-stained ash, and after the intricacies of the wrought iron it seemed plain, simple. But the lines were exact and the inlay work flawless.

"Hey, Padre," a man called. "Did you hear from the old lady?"

"Not yet, Marty. I only wrote her yesterday."

"Aw, heck." Marty returned to his work.

"Impatient," Father Hyland explained to Hogan.

The guard looked at the work. "Impatient? And they do that kind of job?"

"Maybe we're teaching them a little." The chaplain smiled.

Using his old system, Joe Hogan thought, not preaching at

them, just giving them jobs to do and pointing out the significance of the labor. It worked.

With his student sculptors about, Cyrus Turner was toiling at a mysterious figure. Its form was extraordinarily squat, and the chaplain viewed it with some alarm.

"What's that going to turn out to be?" he asked.

Turner smiled, resting his elbow on what was presumably a head. "A surprise. It's for the shrine."

"We've put some strange things in shrines already," Father Hyland reminded him. "I don't know how much I can stand!"

"But this is for the shrine up here. It's got to be good."

"Are you having a shrine here?" Joe Hogan asked.

"Certainly. Next spring we start landscaping. Then we'll put the steps in. And the monastery garden."

"Quite a program!"

"The more things in, the more to keep up. That's what's got me worried—how to keep up the work. I'm getting a greenhouse donated, and that will need care. Then there's the choir. That'll go on. But how many statues can you put in a church? And there are only fourteen windows. Eventually they'll all be made. Then what?"

"You'll think of something."

"I'll try. There's got to be something."

As they went along through the art room where men were sketching and where Father Hyland leafed through some of the drawings for the windows, Hogan said, "My gosh, Padre, think what you've done for these men already. They've got skilled trades. They'll be good outside."

"That isn't my first job, Joe. They spend years planning what they'll do when they get out. We have to teach them how to live while they're in here."

"That's a tough assignment."

"I know. But it can be done. Nuns do it, don't they?"

Joe laughed. "That's a little different."

"Mother Angela doesn't think so. The Carmelites chose their cloister and these men didn't. But I know they can. They can still choose this life willingly, if we can teach them what penance means."

"But that's sanctity."

"There are saints in prison."

"I never saw any."

"You weren't looking for them." The priest had again leafed through the drawings, and as he looked at them now he frowned and put them down hastily. "I know there are saints in prison. Think of a life of retribution for one mortal sin! It scares me."

"How do you know so much about it?"

"I was in prison myself for four years."

"Aw, go on. Where?"

"In the seminary. Don't laugh. We were pretty cloistered, and I almost escaped once. Only I went back—and made the choice."

They came to the last of the schools where Carlos and a man named Jack were making experiments in stained glass. As they entered Jack was screaming, "Get away from that thing! Get your head out of it. How would you look with no ears?"

Carlos raised his flushed face from the kiln.

"Having trouble?" the chaplain asked.

"You bet. This thing won't work."

"He wants to blow us all up," Jack explained quietly.

"No. Only with electricity, what can you do? All the glass sticks."

"Do you need a model? I could get Dominic on a keg——"

"Not this time. And you can't kick the kiln either. It's too hot."

Hogan had been examining things. "What's this contraption?"

"It's the first electrical kiln in the world. Carlos invented it. There were hazards with the other kilns, so this is the first electric smelter."

"It's a smelter that don't smelt," Carlos said.

"Yeh." Jack was gloomy. "It'll blow us all up."

"How does it work?"

"It don't," Carlos said.

The priest went over to it. "You see this? That's a piece of flesh glass or it *was*——"

"Until I ruined it."

"Until Carlos ruined it. He ruins everything. Like the painting of the Good Thief."

The triumphant smile came back into the corners of Carlos's eyes.

"So," the chaplain went on, "you take the flesh glass and you smear it with liquid iron, like this, then with thin brown clay. Then you let it dry. Pick off the features from the surface with a dry brush—just the opposite to painting. Then you place it in the kiln at 1300 degrees Fahrenheit——"

"And blow us up," Jack muttered.

"And if you aren't blown up——"

"The glass sticks to the plates." Carlos was again despondent.

"Say," Hogan asked the chaplain, "how do you know so much about it?"

"Oh, I learned. They taught me down at Rambush's."

"You mean you went down there and learned this business?"

"Certainly. Why not?"

"And the rest of these things? Iron—draftsmanship——"

"I don't know much about them. I just thought I'd better find out how things were done, so I could teach the men. They know a lot more than I do now."

"Oh yeah?" Jack interjected. "That's what he says."

"I wish I knew how to solve your problem now. Have you any other ideas?"

"Just one, Pops," Carlos said. "If that doesn't work——"

"It will. It's got to. And did you ever notice, when a thing has got to, it does?"

On the way down the hill, after their inspection tour, Joe Hogan stopped at the first gate and said, "I think it's wonderful. And why the top kicks don't see what you're doing—don't open this gate for you—I don't know."

"Better not fight for me, Joe. It's dangerous."

"How do you know?"

"These locked gates. The silent treatment. Things like that."

And though Joe Hogan said nothing more, he knew. He had seen the symptoms. The first two wardens had understood Father Hyland. But there had been such rapid turnovers in the last year or so that it was no wonder that the incoming prison governors could be disturbed. They would be thinking, "Who is running this prison anyhow?" And that was dangerous, if you lived as they did in a great castle with fourteen flunkies. It was dangerous, too, to have had as much publicity as the Church of the Good Thief had had. Even this last *Reader's Digest* story gave no credit to the wardens—all to the Padre of the Thieves.

When they reached the warmth of the long, red-brick passageway, Joe Hogan said, "Look, Father, whatever happens, I'm with you."

"I know that."

"After all, I built the church for you, didn't I?"

The guard could not understand why Father Hyland stopped suddenly, looked at him a moment, and said, "No, Joe. Bud Horne built it—all alone," and laughed and went on.

He could not understand the priest. That was a funny remark. Who else had been chief engineer? He didn't want credit for himself, but why did the padre have to say that? And who was Bud Horne?

He could scarcely be expected to know that in the tower of the church Bud Horne was agreeing with Father Hyland. As far as he knew, he alone was responsible for the church.

And he certainly did not know that in New York, Joe Madden, proudly displaying the model of the Church of the Good Thief, was saying, "Well, youse guys get the low-down on this—it never would of been, except for the Marquis of Fifty-sixth Street."

And in Albany Mr. Colpoys, in the men's bar of the Ten

Eyck, was remarking that there had been a wonderful accomplishment up there at Dannemora. "But you know, the first one who was ever approached was myself and I say this in all modesty, I gave that young man some good advice. I'm glad he followed it."

And in Hollywood, California, a parolee was saying to Mr. Darryl Zanuck and Mr. John Ford, "Of course, with all this publicity and everything, I'm naturally interested. I had something of a hand in it. In fact, I guess I started it. You see, the padre said to me——"

And on Long Island——

2. Mrs. Cassidy, in her flat in Brooklyn, pushed the tears back into her eyes. She had received the letter this morning and it said that Cassidy was coming home.

Fifteen years ago she had prayed for this every day, but now she did not know what to do about it at all. The children had grown up and she had not told them much about their father. They had their nice friends too. Maybe they would have to move out of the neighborhood and start in all over again in Queens or the Bronx, and she wouldn't like that because she would miss the monsignor and the Altar and Rosary Society.

But mainly she felt bad because of these thoughts. She would confess them and all, come First Friday. She ought to be glad Cassidy was getting out. God knows he deserved the breaks, and he was a changed man, the pastor up there at Dannemora had written her.

Now she took out Father Hyland's letter telling her about Dan. It was a beautiful letter—not so fresh as it had been when it came, but you could still read the swell things the priest up there had said about Dan. She had never let anyone else read it. But now she would have to share it with the kids.

Maybe they'd be glad of it, too, she hoped, that their father had started the devotion to the Infant of Prague and that he had built a church. That's what the holy priest said. Their father, Dan Cassidy, had built a church.

Well, he had, hadn't he?

3. On the next bright day, when the February snow lay brilliant all around, Father Hyland was saying his prayers of thanksgiving after Mass. He saw Dominic, kneeling before the high altar, looking up at the painting of Saint Dismas.

"Praying to himself," he thought, smiling. But he dismissed the idea as unworthy. There was too much childlike faith in Dominic's expression, and if he was seeing himself there, it was as the portrait of what he wanted to be and was trying to be.

The priest could not banish Dominic from his mind. He had learned long since that the only way to get rid of a distraction in prayer was to give in to it, so he began to pray for Dominic. He always did this now.

Dominic had no distractions. He had only one thought. The Board of Parole was meeting and he and Cassidy were to appear before it. Cassidy had no worries. He was a good mechanic when he was sober, and he would have a job to go back to. Besides, he had the Bambino.

Well, Dominic had Dismas. But no trade. He couldn't go out and pose for holy pictures, could he? But he had Dismas, and Dismas had the padre.

He waited, until his knees hurt, for Father Hyland to get through with his prayers, and then he followed him past the guard who always sat in the outer vestibule, into the lower office in the tower.

"Padre," he said simply, "Saint Dismas wants you should get me a job."

"Yes," the priest replied soberly. "He just told me."

"He did?"

"Yes. You and a lot of others."

"Did he tell you how?"

"He gave me an idea."

"That's swell. So I get out?"

"Yes. You will. While the war work is on——"

"I knew Saint Dismas wouldn't let me down."

Yes. There was need for labor now. But after the war? Would there be a reversion to the old days when men could wait here indefinitely because of the very natural revulsion of employers to hire parolees? Then what about men like Dominic?

Something permanent would have to be done. A group must be organized which would be willing to accept ex-convicts for labor. It must realize that some would fail. Be ready for that. Provide employment which would not present too many hazards. It demanded heroes.

That day he determined that such a group would exist.

He had looked around the church. So the people outside, and even Joe Hogan within, had thought that, with the completion of the building, the task was done. It was only beginning. And now he needed assistance, the help of prayer from those who understood.

It was then that he missed Max Bergner.

He had not seen much of the old man, but at such moments as this, he remembered, he had always gone down to the idle-companies' tier. He had reached his hand through the bars and asked for prayers.

Now who was left? Even Mother Angela seemed too far away. There must be someone here—someone who was holy.

Then he remembered. Tom Riordan in the State Hospital. He had become a man of prayer.

So Father Hyland threw his great black cape about him and started down the shining hill toward the Hospital for the Criminal Insane to ask prayers of a murderer, to begin a friendship of spiritual dependence on one who would always be here, because his term was life.

CHAPTER TWO

The room in which Tom Riordan had found his life was not much larger than a closet. It had a barred window, two chairs, and an ash tray. As yet there were not many books, but those which had been sent to him he had bound in brown paper and had glued their frail pages together with transparent tape. Many people sent books to the prison library. Few ever gave a thought to the hospital.

He had not expected Father Hyland, but he was a day ahead in his work, and was ready for him. He had been following a correspondence course for catechists, and each week it would be ready for the chaplain, who read it, discussed it, and sent it on for him. In addition he had gained a fair knowledge of Latin and was beginning Greek.

"Tom," the priest said when he came in, "I've got a favor to ask you."

"Me? What can I do?"

"Just about everything. But first I want to know what you find hardest here."

"Fear."

"I never thought you were afraid."

"I'm not. People are afraid of me."

"Why?"

"I'm a religious nut. We're the worst kind. First, the guards think we're dangerous. Then that seeps into the inmates. They get afraid too. Nobody reasons about much in here. We just feel things. You can smell fear all around the way animals do. And animals turn on you if they think you're afraid. Or if they sense danger. That's the way we act."

"I've seen some things. The desire to destroy the weak."

"Yes. Only animals know their own power; human beings invent it. If they're nobody, can't do anything, they build a world for themselves where they are somebody. That's where the delusions start."

"If you are somebody, Tom, does it help?"

"Do you remember saying that to me? Yes. It helped."

"I'm glad. You know what I'm talking about, then. We don't need just jobs for the men. We need something inside them."

"Sure. But like what?"

"Like taking this fear that bothers you—offering it up. Every day for one soul. Not just for everybody, but for one individual. Will you do that, Tom?"

Tom Riordan was silent for a moment. Then he looked up. "You could *live* for a day like that. You'd have something to give. Not much, but——"

"Not much. Only your life."

The priest rose. "I'm going to make the rounds. I'll come back with a list of names, and you can start with one of them. Then afterward we can branch out, over in the prison. That is, if this works with you."

Tom laughed. "O.K.," he said. "I'll be your spiritual guinea pig."

"I know this isn't a fair test." The priest smiled. "I'm not taking many chances with you. But we've got to make men realize that their days are important. They've got to have a sense of dignity—in something."

Tom remembered what he had seen, how the priest, day after day, had spoken to the men who were interminably sweeping, dusting, mopping—one man riding on a homemade waxer as on a Roman chariot, while four men pulled him— and how the priest would stop and tell them that their work was good. He did it lightly, but it made a difference.

"It's the answer, Father," Tom said. "Like what I'm trying to do."

"I know. That's the answer too."

Going on his way, the priest thought of what Tom's answer was. Like all prisoners, Tom chose grandiloquent names for things and he called his reading program, in which he had interested such men as were not afraid of him, "Bibliotherapy." Still, that was no sillier than some of the words the psychiatrists used. The chaplain recalled what brought that to mind.

Yesterday a very dignified gentleman in prison gray had come to him, explaining that he was a college graduate and therefore different. Caught in that horrible experiment of Mr. Hoover's and delighted that at last his fellow countrymen had revoked their prohibition, he had said. Then getting to the point he had—how had he put it?—"elicited aid."

"You see, Père, I'm bothered by these psychoanalysts, as

they call 'em. God have mercy on them for mangling the Greek."

"What's the trouble?"

"Parataxis they're talking about. Parataxis, mind you! And if these—these"—he paused for a word—"these *intruders* would stop wasting time discovering that I was frightened by a hobbyhorse at the age of six and employ my capabilities, we'd all be better off."

"What are your capabilities?"

"I *could* teach your choir scholastic Latin. It would help if they knew the difference between *factum* and *genitum*. They don't seem to."

So now, along with Reinald Werrenrath, who came twice a week to instruct Bill Martin, the cultured bootlegger was coaching the men in Latin declensions and was no longer bothered by the mangling of the Greek.

He had found his adjustment. So had Tom Riordan. But what of others?

Tony smiled and did not speak. The man in the canvas bag smiled, smiled. And the young boy who had been all right yesterday screamed, "Take me out of here! Change me!"

"Where to, Billy?"

"California."

"That's too far."

"All right. Make it Ward 14!"

Behind him the feet shuffled and a voice whispered, "Padre, remember me? I worked on your church. I built the church. Remember? Then they didn't have anything else for me to do. I *was* all right, wasn't I?"

"Yes. You were all right."

"You know what they did? They hypnotized me. That's what happened outside too. That's why I jumped parole. I never did anything until I got hypnotized."

"How did they do it?"

"They made me stare at a wall. All day. Nothing else. Stare at a wall——"

"What can I do for you?"

"Unhypnotize me, Padre. Bless me."

He blessed him and went on.

Around the next turn the man in the hospital nightshirt said, "Make them stop forging my name to outgoing mail. They put my name on crazy things I never wrote. The doctors read them and they think a guy wrote those crazy things is crazy. Here. Here's a tab. This—what—I—wrote."

The tab was addressed to Mr. Dewey. It was a formula for blowing up the White House and making Mr. Dewey President. It was secret and confidential. It also asked for parole.

In the confined company on the far west corridor Old Timmy was picking daisies. He picked daisies all day long, and usually, when they opened his cell, he would give the guard a great garland of daisies, but today he did not feel like giving daisies away. He stamped on the daisies and would not make a daisy chain, and then he threw himself on his pallet and wept. He said bad things to the guard, and the guard came over, walking on the daisies, crushing them, and tried to make him stand up.

Timmy was very upset with the guard. He bit his hand to make him drop the daisies, and the guard slapped him around.

"Stop that!" Father Hyland ordered.

"He bit me!"

"I know. Come out of there. Close the door."

"You've got to do that sometimes, Padre."

"Or else leave them alone when they're that way. How old is Timmy?"

"He's pretty old."

"Yes. And he's been picking daisies for ten years. Know why?"

"No."

"Because for years Timmy hadn't seen grass. Then they made him a trusty. He saw some daisies on the warden's lawn. So he picked them. They put him back in solitary. But Timmy's had his daisies ever since. Leave him alone."

"But he bit me!"

"I know. I know."

There were the calls from the left-hand cell, calls that always came, hour after hour, whenever he went by, from the naked waste of manhood that was there. "I want a priest! Get me a priest!"

"I'll try again," Father Hyland said. The guard unlocked the gate and the priest went in. A scream of oaths, obscenities, foul words, and cries. Always the same.

"What you trying to do? You're not a priest. Get out of here! You're trying to get a confession out of me. You can't fool me—dressed up that way. Get out!"

When, despairing, the priest left, he could hear, all down the corridor, the call, "I want a priest! Get me a priest!"

Then back to Tom Riordan without a list of names, because this had been a bad day and he had met no one in this moon phase who could be helped. Just as he turned through the door to the auditorium, a man stopped him. His eyes seemed sane.

"Father, I'd like a favor. I'm up for parole. I'd like for you to introduce me to somebody that'd get me a job."

"Certainly. Who?"

"You know. If I was a gangster I could get a job. Five years ago I was up for parole. Who did I know? You know gangsters. I want you to fix me up with your buddy."

"Which one?"

"Shh. Let me whisper." He leaned close to the priest's ear and then screamed with all his lungs. "Al Capone! Al Capone!"

Oh yes, yes, the priest thought on his way back to the sanity of Tom Riordan, underneath this madness was so much truth. It would have been a way out for this man five years ago. He was right.

"Tom," he said when he reached the office, "I can't give you names of men on this side today. It's a bad day for them. We'll start on the other side, after all. Just pray they won't have the things happen to them that bring them over here."

"You said you'd give me one name."

"I will. This case is different. Offer up tomorrow for a man

of mine who is still bitter and crafty and sly. There was just
once I thought I had him, Tom. Just once, I thought——"
"What's his name?"
"Bud Horne."

2. In White Plains, Mr. Stein was composing a letter in his
mind. "I am not happy that I should take into employ your
friend Mr. Bud Horne recommended to me by you from
Clinton State Prison. I have no such wish to have this person
in my business which is to date a respectable enterprise and
has no dealings with such types as jailbirds. If you are not
satisfied with my repayment of the loan made me on the
twenty-first instant . . ."
What he actually wrote was:

Marco and Company.
39-38 K Street
White Plains
New York.
    Gentlemen:
        In receipt of yours of the fourteenth, allow me to say that I
shall be happy to find a position for Mr. Bud Horne whom you so
highly recommended. There will be a vacancy here after the first of
the year and I shall immediately forward same information to Mr.
Horne at the address you have provided. Thanking you for your
continued interest in my affairs, I am,

                              Yours, et cetera,
                              Milton Stein, Esq.

3. Once the priest had nearly found Bud Horne. Only once.
But there had been a moment and a closeness when he had
thought—— But that was a long time ago. Nothing since.
    It was the night they were finishing the church and the
men had been allowed to stay out of their cells after dark,
working to be through on time. He and Bud had been the
last to come down the hill. Bud always was last.
    The night was cool and crisp, a night of clear air before the
rising of the moon, when the dome of heaven was vaulted

with stars. There was no illumination in the prison save for a dimness from the narrow corridors of the tiers. There wasn't a sound.

The priest had gone on for some paces before he found that Bud Horne had stopped. He turned, saw him standing on the hillside, went back to him. For the only time he put his hand on Bud's shoulder.

"What are you looking at, Bud?"

Through a long silence Bud did not answer, and when at last he spoke his voice was not as the priest had ever heard it before.

"The stars," he said.

Above them the only lights, gleaming, brilliant.

"Millions of them. The stars."

"How long since you've seen the stars, Bud?"

"Twenty years. I've had an inside cell, Pops. Twenty years."

The priest did not speak again until they were ready to go together down the hill. Bud spoke once.

"The stars."

4. It had stopped snowing in New York and the stars had come out. Max Bergner, hastening from his job on Barclay Street, kept looking at them. He could not get enough of them. But he had to hurry, because there might be another letter.

He had tried many religious orders already. The Jesuits had told him that they would take him after three years if he persevered; at Maryknoll they thought he was too old for their work; the Trappists doubted that he could stand the rigors of their life; the Benedictines, most gracious of all, could not place him at the moment but would keep him in mind.

Better, he thought sometimes, to be back at Dannemora. He had made a cloistered life for himself there, always under obedience, always doing the will of God. But someday there would be a letter accepting him in a religious order. Someday.

There was none that day either.

5. On an unseasonably warm morning in March, Dominic and Cassidy had gone out free and Bud Horne sat in the upper tower office brooding. On his desk was the new order. No more pets were to be kept in prison. Not even birds.

Greeney had just gone into the garden and was morosely scuffling wet black leaves away from the bulbs. Even the sight of new wings flying from the south could not move him, though Cyrus Turner paused in what he was doing to watch him. And Bud Horne knew how Greeney felt. He was unstirred by it because he had his own plans. The freeing of Dominic and Cassidy tasted bad in his mouth.

Even Dominic had got out. It was easy now. He himself was not due for parole, but he had better work fast and get executive clemency. He wanted out.

Before him lay a pile of papers. There was the complete draft of a book to be written on the building of the church bulking beside the vast, laborious outline of the financial budgeting program. And there was his own time chart.

"Look, Chaplain," he would say, "here's the extra time I spent for you. Would you sign it?" The padre might see through it but he'd sign all right. Once there was the signature, it could be used to get clemency. The governor would be a sucker for anything like that. The press would eat it up.

He heard the chaplain's footsteps on the iron stairs that led up to the tower. He would tackle him now. The padre was in good humor over an article that had appeared in the *Reader's Digest* about the church.

"Bud! Bud!" The priest's voice was calling him.

"I'm up here."

"Good. I'm going to look at the stained glass. Call me there."

"Wait a minute!" It was always the same. If you could only get him to stay in the same place for a while.

"I can't now——" Father Hyland was saying. Then he stopped in mid-sentence. He had made a resolve, which he was always breaking, that no external work would interfere with individuals. "All right," he said, "if it *is* just a minute."

"I want you to look at this time sheet. I wish you'd sign it and say it's correct."

"Good. Good." The priest picked up the papers and began to read them hastily. "But Carlos wants me for the stained glass. I've got to—— Say, what's this all about anyway?"

"Just the extra hours I put in on the church work."

"We all spent extra hours——" the priest began. But that wasn't the point. Everybody had a right to recognition. He himself had been pleased with the *Digest* article. If this was what Bud wanted, he could have it. Then the telephone rang, and Father Hyland answered it. Always something, Bud Horne thought.

"Bud! Make a note of this, will you? Cohen in the shops wants some felt."

"What for?"

"I don't know. For a machine. I'll take a look at it."

Bud wrote, "Get some felt." Then he saw that the priest was leaving.

"Hey! How about my papers?"

"I'll look at them later." He stuffed them into the pocket of his cassock. "Got to rush now. Carlos and Jack need me." And he was off.

He found them, their faces aglow over the kiln. "Don't talk," Carlos whispered to him. "We think we've got it this time, Pops. Give us five, ten minutes."

The priest used the time by looking over the sketches for the Stations. They were made by different men and the head of Christ in each differed. Each was reverent and each beautiful, but there were fourteen Christs. It was good. The concept of the sacred visage varied with every man's eye that saw it. There was no reason for consistency in these windows.

But what he had not noticed before was the faces of the soldiers and of the jeering mobs. As he thumbed through the sketches this time, he was struck by the horror of these portrayals. Here was unmitigated evil looking out at him. And the terrifying thing was that he recognized most of the originals not as caricatures, but as accurate representations of his men.

He had never known them like this. In the years he had been here he had often wondered what they would look like in a holdup, at the moment of murder, and he realized now that he had never seen them so. Was this the way they really looked, when their priest was not near, marred with treachery and lust and greed and hatred?

No. He could not allow himself to think of them thus. He closed the book of sketches hastily.

Then the moment was broken, and he was glad. Carlos had cried, "We've got it! Let it cool!"

Father Hyland went over to where the two were examining the new glass. It was flawless, the color perfect.

"How did you do it? What did you use?"

Jack answered. "Alum. Carlos found it. Alum. Pour it on the hot iron and the glass doesn't stick."

"I never heard of alum! I never heard of such a process," the priest said.

"Gee, Pops," Carlos answered, "neither did we. We never even read it."

"Have you got it written down? Have you got the formula?"

"Yeah! I got it, Pops!" Carlos leaped across the room in his excitement and almost danced back with a little brown notebook. "See! It's all here."

Hastily Father Hyland examined it. Alum. Powdered and sprinkled alum. Simple!

"It didn't blow up," Jack shouted, "and she doesn't stick."

"Carlos," he said, "you've found something. This time you've done it."

The expression he saw on Carlos's face eased the nightmare impression of the sketches. It was as if suddenly he saw years of self-doubt lifted off and a person emerge.

"Hurry up!" Carlos cried. "Get the men in here. We got to begin!" And as the priest went out to call in his school of stained-glass makers, Jack was already firing the kiln, Carlos was sprinkling the alum, and the stained-glass making was begun.

When Father Hyland returned with his crew, Jack and

Carlos warned him that the first panel would surprise him. It did.

What he saw was a replica of a rubicund man with a cigar in his mouth, incongruous and delightful, in stained glass.

"What in all that's wonderful is this?" he cried.

"Don't you get it?"

"Oh yes, yes!" He got it. It was a stained-glass panel, not of Saint Dismas, not of the Little Flower, but, of all people, their own saint, Joe Madden.

"Boys," he said solemnly, "this is a great event. There is only one other like it—a man with a cigar in stained glass. It is in a cathedral or something in England. Here is to the both of them: Churchill and Madden!"

They pounded the priest on the back. They laughed. They screamed until Cyrus Turner, at his sketching next door, was disturbed.

"Winny Churchill and Joe Madden!" they cried. "Churchill and Madden!"

6.   At his club in London, Brendon O'Malley took another whisky and water. He fancied that he had just been made a very lucrative offer and it disgusted him.

Oh, it had been suavely put. Since his arrival here he had been received as a temporary gentleman and he had known that there had been some purpose behind everything. Though there was more reason for his social acceptance since his engagement to Laura. She belonged.

Yet, he recalled, only because he had been taken up in the better circles had he met her, and now he wondered about that. Had they really accepted him for himself, a romantic Irishman from the Far West, a glamorous flier who had done gallantly in Spain, and who had since had more than his share of Jerries? Who went on hazardous missions to Africa and America and who was dashing in his tailored R.A.F. uniform?

He was not conceited, but now, he realized, he had begun to think of himself as all those things. It had been so easy. He had a personal valet, a snug little flat, these clubs. He had laughed, thinking how his mother had slaved in her white uniform for far less than this. And it had not taken him long to expect to be called "Sir." He was a good officer. His men respected him. Some even liked him.

He had never wondered about it until tonight.

Of course he had known what was going on, but it had never touched him before—it was something that happened to other people. These men made it sound like a game.

"It's a bit of fun, and it merely outwits terrible persons at borders of places. I don't think it's harmful."

"But it isn't legal!" Immediately Brendon regretted saying that.

"Not quite. But so little is. But what harm? I've something belongs to me, I want it in another place, and why should a stupid government seize half its value?"

Another gentleman smiled understandingly. "Right. I could easily share that viewpoint. I'm in rather a tight spot myself, you know. Got some quite valuable things in Africa I'd much rather have in America."

Then the first gentleman had looked squarely at Brendon, just the faintest trace of amusement in his eyes. "That's your run, isn't it, O'Malley?"

It was then that Brendon got up quickly and went to the bar for a bracer. He had been seethingly angry. But now that he had his drink, he was merely disgusted.

Strange. Why had he thought of his mother in her white uniform, her low, sensible shoes? Why hadn't he stayed *himself*?

Golly, he remembered suddenly, he hadn't written her in seven months.

7. The time for the uncrating of the first statue had come, and Carlos and Jack and Cyrus Turner stood triumphantly by.

"What's it going to be?" Joe Hogan whispered to Father Hyland.

"I don't know. Remember, I doubted about it? They punished me. I had to wait."

Then the box was knocked away and they could see.

It was the figure of a boy in prison uniform. Carefully the men placed it in position before the empty niche where Our Lady would be. The reason for the squatness they had observed in the unfinished block was now apparent. The boy was kneeling.

The workmanship was still crude and not a little heavy, but there was an honesty here, and the significance of a criminal where, in a grotto of the Immaculate Conception, the children of Lourdes were usually found, was a stinging in the eyes.

"You've done it now, Cyrus. That's it."

"Thank you, Father. Now I'm ready—for Our Lady."

He passed the sketch which he had planned to the priest. It was a strange face yet somehow familiar.

"I've seen this before somewhere. Who is it?"

"Our Lady."

"I know, Cy. But who was the model?"

"You wouldn't know her, Father. Her name is Mona."

"Perhaps not. But I've seen her somewhere."

Cyrus Turner smiled crookedly. "All right then, I'll tell you." He glanced over to where Carlos was standing, not looking at the new sculpture but contemplating the windows where his stained glass would be. "You've seen her in every Virgin and Child that Carlos has drawn. Now do you understand?"

Yes. That was it. It was the same lady that he had seen in Carlos's paintings.

"I see," the priest said. "But I'm surprised that you copied Carlos. You are usually so original."

"I didn't," Turner replied slowly. "We both drew from life—the same girl. I thought I would kill him when I found out about it. But now I've done this instead."

"Does he know?"

"Yes. We both know now."

They were interrupted by a call from Bud Horne, whose

imperturbability had somehow been shattered. He was actually running around the corner of the church.

"Hey, Chaplain! There's a long-distance call for you."

"All right. I'll come."

"But gee—it's person to person."

"All right. All right!"

"But you don't get it! It's from Hollywood!"

CHAPTER THREE

After he had packed his mother in the car and they were off, it seemed to Ambrose Hyland that it had been a matter of moments since the telephone call had come, but actually several weeks had elapsed. They had been filled with negotiations out of which only one thing had emerged: that Hollywood wanted to make a picture about the Church of the Good Thief and that it was necessary for him to go to California.

He had not really believed it until he got as far West as Denver, but from there on his mission began to take focus. Even his mother seemed to be facing the idea that this was more than a picnic jaunt. The first day out, he remembered, she had produced a neatly packed lunch and a thermos bottle full of coffee.

"Might as well stop here," she had said. "I brought something to eat. We have quite a distance ahead of us, Ambrose."

"Yes," he replied. "About three thousand miles."

"Nothing like a good home-cooked lunch to start off with." She uncorked a pickle jar and dumped the contents onto a paper plate. "Better save the bottle to carry water in through the desert," she said. "We might run out. And the next town we come to we'll get mustard."

That is the way it had been all the time. Nothing could daunt her. The railroad trains that had seemed to run straight through the cabin in Eagle, Colorado, had kept him awake all night, but she was up before him and had breakfast ready.

"I didn't mind those trains at all," she said over the sausage.

"I thought they were kind of company. Made me think I was in New York."

She took everything as a matter of course, refusing even to be impressed by the Rockies. "Used to mountains all my life," she had said. "Grew up in them. These here are a little taller, that's all."

Only once, when they had topped a hairpin turn at sunset and had come out above tree level to a scene of unmatched magnificence and her son had stopped the car, she caught her breath; but all she said was, "It's a pity those poor fellows of yours have to live in the city. We've got an awful lot of room in this country of ours." And once in the salt plateaus of Utah she had said, "Yes. It's true. They *have* got more sky out here."

He understood that. After his years behind the prison gates these wide expanses were a relief, an exultation. Their vastness made him realize his previous confinement as never before.

But his mother tempered any excitement which he might feel. She made light of the motion picture. It was a movie. They had a change of bill three times a week in Chateaugay. Must be an awful lot of movies.

As for himself, this meant everything. The picture must be a story about prison, not just another prison story—stereotyped, unreal. There had been so many about gangsters and riots and crime. This must be regeneration.

He thought of it as a crusade, not for any cause of prison reform, but simply that his black sheep might be understood with the understanding which the years had brought him. Few on the outside listened to him when he talked; their opinions were preconceived, and prisoners were catalogued safely, set in neat little compartments of public prejudice.

—I suppose they all try to take you in, some way or another.
—It must be pretty heartbreaking work, isn't it?
—Do any of them actually reform?
—This parole system now. It never seems to work, does it?

—They tell me the young ones learn all about crime in prison.

—All most of them want is three square meals a day.

—Of course you can't say those fellows react the same as we would.

—The best thing to do would be to give them all the electric chair.

—Criminal traits run in families. Don't you think we ought to stop that?

—Yeah. You can talk about them, but what about their victims?

He wanted to answer those objections and show what things were really like. Already he could see the great scenes of the men tearing down the walls, of the craftsmen's booths around the church as it was going up, of the vested choir singing at the dedication, under the Good Thief which Carlos had painted. He wanted the moment at the gate where he had said good-by to Cassidy and Dominic, knowing in his heart that those two, at least, would never be back. Above all he wanted one shot of Max Bergner praying at night in his cell.

Then he said aloud, "I know what I want, Mother. You know, they call the prison bureau the 'Department of Correction.' Sometimes I think people want it called the 'Department of Detention.' It isn't. It's *correction.*"

They were driving then at night through a high plateau in Nevada, the mountains far distant like cut-out stage scenery, black jags against the moonlight.

"I know, Ambrose," his mother said. "Don't get me wrong. I'm just different from most people. Can't get excited about what hasn't happened yet. I remember when your father came a-courtin'. There I was, a little country girl and he was a big, handsome man from the city. Don't know what I was looking for. But that was before I got him. Afterward—well, you know how it was with us."

Yes. He knew how it had been with them.

She was going on. "So that's the way I'm going to feel about your movie. I'll love it when I see it, sitting looking at it."

Without pausing to change the subject she asked, "Where are we going to stay tonight?"

"Reno," he answered.

"Reno. The poor things." And he knew she was thinking about the joy of her own marriage and of all unhappy women.

2. Mona's laughter had been bright and brittle as the sun on her flaming hair. She had run along the beach at Provincetown and the boys and girls had stopped their art chatter to smile and wave at her. She had gone running on, a beautiful bronze figure.

Now she flung herself down on the dunes. She would go all to pieces. She did when she was alone.

Last night at the party she had been so pert, when they talked as freely as they always did here. "Just a gun moll at heart," she had cried. "Two-time Mona they call me."

She threw their thinking back into their faces. They all knew about Cyrus Turner and they all knew that she had turned Carlos in. Most places, no one would mention it, but they came out with everything in Provincetown. Let them. She was sick of them all. Forever painting the dunes. Things that had been done a thousand times. Giving the idea that to sell, to make money on their paintings, their books, their music, was the mortal sin. All of them phonies. Provincetown had had its day. Now it had nothing left but words.

All right. She could say them too. She could keep up the front until it was necessary to run away and crumple up like this and see Carlos's face looking at her when she testified. He had looked like a cow. She loathed the recollection but she could not get it out of her mind. It was funny. She never could see Turner as she saw Carlos. Maybe she had loved Turner after all.

Over and over she kept thinking the same thought. "They're better off up there. They got the break, not me."

Everybody had a kind of sympathy for convicts, and there was a movement afoot to get Turner out. But who had any idea what she had gone through? Did they ever think what it was like for the girl outside, untouched, unpunished, as far as society could see?

She scratched at the sand dunes as if they were Carlos's face. He was making out all right. Painting. Stained glass. She had read his sloppy letters before she had burned them, unanswered. Making her into the Immaculate Conception of the penitentiary. That was a laugh.

God knows what those two men were thinking about her up there in prison. She didn't know or care. Who ever thought about her anyway? Who knew what she was going through?

They were better off up there.

The wedding at Farm Street had been beautiful, Laura O'Malley remembered, but the time afterward with Brendon had been so short and she had missed him dreadfully through the months when he had been in Africa. She had tried to fill her days with war work but it was not enough. The excitement she had once felt at the blitzes had passed away until they seemed almost a routine and one scurried to the shelters quite as a matter of course.

But you would never get used to the worry of having your man away, she told herself. And there was something the matter with Brendon. She could name the moment, just before their marriage, when something had happened. A light had gone out in her.

"You know," he had said, "there was something I intended to tell you today."

"Was there?"

"Mm-mm. It slipped my mind, I guess." He was trying to keep the conversation light.

"What was it, Brendon?"

"I forgot to mention that I love you. I do, you know."

"That's very nice of you. And it's really jolly that just by chance I rather like you."

"And by the way——"

She knew that it was coming. "Yes?"

"You'll have to wait for me a bit afterward. I won't be around for a while. You see, a buddy of mine is in a jam. Just routine matter, but I've got to cover for him. It will keep me in Africa. Do you mind?"

"Of course I mind. But I wouldn't have you otherwise. You won't be involved, will you?"

"No." He spoke too hastily. "Of course not. But if anything is said, wait till you hear my side, will you?"

"I wouldn't have to. For me there is no other side."

That was all that had been said. But she could have screamed this afternoon when a woman had sympathized with her. "It's worse for the wives waiting, deary."

It was Brendon she was worried about. Not herself. There was something terribly wrong.

If Millie Green hadn't had the baby she would have been all right. She hadn't wanted Allan's baby anyhow, and there were states that agreed that a woman could get a divorce if her husband was in prison, but did they have a solution for a woman with a baby? Oh no. It tied her down.

The other girls who worked beside her in the factory, now that the war was on, could have a good time and not have to worry. Why should she be different? It didn't matter so much that Greeney was up in Dannemora. Nobody blamed her for that. He had brought it on himself. Then why did she have to take it on the chin just because he had gone wrong? She had to lead her own life. It was the only one she'd ever have, wasn't it? And this way, how could she get another man?

Mrs. Cassidy knew there wasn't a better man than her husband anywhere in the world when he wasn't drinking and all, but you couldn't blame him too much for that now. She thought that any man would take to the bottle if he'd been through what Dan had and him not able to go out to the taverns at all because the parole men would be after him. Better anyhow that he took a wee nip at home.

Ever since they had moved here to Third Avenue where

the el came right into your room every night it hadn't been any better. She had thought that when she gave up the old neighborhood, people might leave Cassidy alone.

They hadn't though. She couldn't understand men that would go where somebody was working and tell them they shouldn't have jailbirds around. The boss had known it all the time anyway, but he said he couldn't keep Dan if all the other men on the construction knew about him, so he had to let him go.

Was it any wonder now that Cassidy was taking to the bottle? It was a thing could happen to anybody, and she'd like to know if the rest of them who got out of Dannemora did any better at all?

3. Far down below in a vast semicircle the golden lights of San Francisco began to mingle with the sunset. This was the hour to be here at the Top of the Mark, Father Hyland thought—and to be here alone. The exultation and the serenity of place and moment came as a climax to a day when he had lived through three magnificent seasons—a winter storm, monumental and dangerous over Brenner Pass, a golden autumn down the western slope, summer and palm trees in Sacramento. And now this, and what it meant to him.

He did not know how anyone could have discovered that he was to register at the Saint Francis, but he had not been there long before the message had come. It was from one of his former inmates who wanted urgently to see him today and had set the hour for this twilight rendezvous at the Mark Hopkins.

Even in that invitation he had felt a triumph, for he had heard how well this man was doing on the West Coast. He was always glad to see what he called his "alumni," and they knew it, and were beginning to track him down wherever he went.

He had been glad to have had a few moments alone, watching as the purple shadows crept up the steepness of the hills and the lights of the buildings and of the Golden Gate unfolded into patterns. He was not even thinking, but living an experience as one did at a concert of music.

How much he had missed, he thought without regret, living so many years within prison walls, but how well worth while it had been. He would not have exchanged those years for all the symphonies and plays in the world. He had been in the heart of great drama, and though it was often tragedy, still there were moments of triumph like this when he would meet at least one who had succeeded.

The waiter was hovering over him now, telling him that a friend was inquiring about his table.

And there he was.

He would not have recognized him had he not been fore-warned, he looked so different from the man he had remembered behind the gates. And as he came forward it was obvious that his whole manner had changed, for this man had about him the unmistakable aura of success. He was a man accustomed to the Top of the Mark.

After they had chatted awhile over very excellent martinis and cigars and the dusk had gathered about them, the man said, "I suppose you wondered why I called you?"

"I hope you just wanted to see me."

"That was part of it."

"Something else? Anything I can do?"

His friend laughed. "Not this time. The shoe's on the other foot. I hear you're going to Hollywood."

"Yes. There's a possibility of a movie."

"I know. I have a few friends down there. You may need some ins." He held out a list of names, which, from a hasty glance, looked impressive.

"You know all these people?"

"Sure. That is—my firm does. Might unlock a few doors for you."

"But why should you do this for me?"

The man laughed sharply. "I bet you don't even remember me. You never had any trouble with me. But I did come in to see you once, back in the early days in the old office."

Father Hyland remembered a gangling boy who had come in to see him just once. But that was at a time when it had been important. "Yes," he said, "I remember. I told you to make the most of your prison years—to think of them as time away at school—to take advantage of the educational facilities. Yes. I remember."

"So did I. I got an education. I made good. So now it's my turn."

"That's the story," Father Hyland cried. "That's what we've got to tell everybody in this picture. We want the life of somebody like you!"

Then he unfolded his dream. It poured out of him, this burning desire to portray rehabilitation, true reform. Perhaps he did not realize how long he had talked or perhaps the darkness had come suddenly. He did not know, but in the silence which followed his outburst the sky had gone black and only a vast magic carpet of lights gleamed up from far below.

"Look! Look!" he said, turning around, trying to catch the entire panorama in one movement. "The whole world! It's beautiful!"

There was no response. His companion's figure was slumped in shadow and as he watched the shoulders heaved in a great dry sob. "O God, I tried, Pops. Honest to God, I tried."

It was not right that anyone be so exposed, so vulnerable, like a great raw wound. It was not right here, with the beauty below of inverted stars.

"I can't help you," the man said. "I'm rotten clean through. Not the list. That's straight. Just me."

Then Ambrose Hyland understood. For all this time he had been making a story about a man who had made good. Now this—— "I see," he said.

"You've got it, Pops? I don't want to bluff you. Sure I made good. But the wrong way. I couldn't go it alone. Who's going to talk to us? I had to talk to somebody. Who else was there?"

"Except me." Now all below the priest could see the beauty of the night which had changed until lights danced like bubbles on a surface, below which, like a thick wave, the city lay, squamous and viscous.

"Can't you——" Father Hyland began, but he knew it was futile.

"No. I can't. I tried. Sure, I'm a big shot. I come to do you a favor. That's a laugh." His tone now was thin, ironic. "You can put me in pictures."

The waiter lit a candle. The priest looked at his friend. There was nothing to show crisis, nothing but hard eyes in which lurked sardonic humor.

"I'm back in the rackets, Pops," he said. "But it's the big time now."

CHAPTER FOUR

Recalling his Hollywood experiences afterward, Father Hyland thought that if he had planned a career as an eccentric genius he could not have contrived things better. As far as he knew no one before had thought of him either as a genius or as eccentric.

"All I did," he said later, "was to breathe in and out and things happened. It's that way out there."

His mother and he were late arriving at the Hollywood Plaza, having made side trips to all the missions down the coast. It must have been two in the morning by the time they had registered and were settled in their suite. He was tired from driving and wanted to stretch his legs, never having realized before how much walking he did in the course of his regular work.

It was a beautiful night and he was fascinated by palm trees. He had heard that the Los Angelenos did not care for them, but he found them a novelty. There was a particularly magnificent specimen in front of the Blessed Sacrament Church, and beyond it, in the light of the street lamp, he read the plaque with its religious history of Holy Wood.

This was the Holy Wood set beside the City of the Angels.

All around, towns and streets bore the beautiful names which were familiar to him, the names of saints and of angels, that were peculiarly his own. He felt as much at home here as he did in his own country, which was replete with the memory of Marquette and Jogues; and as he never had felt at home in New England or the rest of the country which was filled with a tradition which was foreign to him. But here Fra Junipero Serra had walked and here the Franciscans still answered the bells of Santa Barbara. That night he fell in love with California; they had had a bad winter at Dannemora.

He walked for a long time, soothed at last and forgetting what he had found so hard to forget—the parolee on the Top of the Mark. Then at last he was tired and went back to Hollywood and Vine.

When he got to the hotel he heard his mother speaking to him from her room. "Ambrose! The telephone. It's been ringing every twenty minutes."

The brisk night voice at the desk said that New York had been calling. Would Father Hyland talk with a man who said he was representing a Mr. Neelet?

"Babyface?" the priest asked casually.

There was a distinct cough at the other end of the wire. "Who? Oh. That who it is?" Then the professional manner resumed. "Will you take it?"

"Surely."

For almost an hour he talked with a Mr. Costa who said that he had been told to get in touch with the padre and give him some dope about Hollywood. There was plenty to be wised up on. He wised him up. And when at last, wearily, Father Hyland put down the phone he was not so sure that he was in the Holy Wood.

It seemed as if it must be about dawn when the telephone rang again, but it was, he saw, about half-past eight. He had been dreaming about the movie.

"Reverend Hyland? There's a registered letter here for you. Shall we send it up?"

"Where's it from?"

"Dannemora, New York. No. That's the registration. It was originally from Pleasantville."

"Oh no," he said sleepily. "I'll get it later. That's just fan mail."

He rolled over and tried to sleep again and then came wide awake, grinning. "Fan mail." What had possessed him to say that? Had he gone Hollywood already?

If he were going to say Mass he had better get up. He had sent a telegram to Monsignor Devlin and he hoped he would be expected.

As he had his hand on the doorknob the phone jangled. The voice from the lobby was hushed, awed. "The studio at Culver City wishes to talk with you. We told them you were engaged, but they insist. Will you take the call?"

"All right. Put them on."

He made a date with a screen writer, an executive and a director for lunch at the Brown Derby at one. He was glad when he came out onto Vine Street to discover that the Brown Derby was directly across from the hotel. He would have plenty of time. Why they had been so respectful in the lobby, he could not quite understand, but he put it down vaguely to the telephone calls.

In the rectory of the church where he went to present himself he was a bit surprised that the monsignor asked for his celebret, the official paper proving that he was a Catholic priest in good standing. He fished it out wonderingly.

"I see, I see," Monsignor Devlin said. "This seems in good order. But how about that church you represent? It has such a strange name."

"Church of the Good Thief? I suppose it is unusual."

The monsignor laughed heartily. "Take a look at this," he said, handing him his own telegram. On it he read, "Church of Good Grief."

"It sounded so typical," the monsignor went on. "We have so many phonies around here. All right. Say your Mass. When you get through we'll have a talk about the industry."

He learned many things before his luncheon, and though he

did not find the Brown Derby quite so pleasant as the Elks Club in Plattsburg and certainly not so colorful as Joe Madden's, the Hollywood men were delightfully enthusiastic. They told him he had something, which he already knew; that this was colossal, which he hoped was so; that it was a natural, which he was relieved to hear.

Then they kept telling him about all the movie people whom he must see. It seemed that one did not simply come to Hollywood, sell a story, and go home. It was more complicated than that and depended a great deal on contacts, publicity, and various impressions on people. Yet most of the names they mentioned he had already heard of in San Francisco.

Finally he passed his list over to the Hollywood executive. He whistled when he saw it. "You mean you can get to all these people?"

"Why, yes," he answered.

"Boys, we're wasting our time. He's got ins nobody has. We should give him advice!"

The director looked at the names. "Get busy, Father. What you sitting here for? Round 'em up. They're your boys."

So Father Hyland started out. But on his way the hat-check girl said that there was a man sitting under the nose of the drawing of Jimmy Durante who wanted to see him. The priest excused himself and went back. He thought he recognized the man at the table, who was smiling broadly at him, but he was not sure.

"You don't know me?"

"I think I should. I've seen you." Vaguely, he thought, vaguely.

"Your parish. Upper New York State. Remember? I know what you're up to. I want to see you about a part. I don't blame you for not recognizing me. They gave me a new hairline and a new set of choppers since I came out here. But I knew you pretty well. I sure had a chance to study you."

A waiter plugged in a telephone and the man turned to it. "See you later. Think it over. Give me a break if you can."

When Father Hyland reached the sidewalk the three Hollywood men asked him, all at once, if he knew whom he had been talking to and told him a name which he recognized from motion-picture advertisements. It was not the same name he had known before. But——

"Yes," he said. "He was an old friend of mine."

"Boy! What a character you turn out to be! And he sits there like he knew nothing."

With that he began his rounds. Day after day he saw people, important people, he supposed, but their reactions were disheartening, and the day at Laguna, where he had corralled several of them, had been the worst of all.

They had been sitting out on the terraces of the Victor Hugo where the flower gardens trailed like brilliant shawls into the Pacific, and all day the men had talked and talked, never waiting long enough to get ideas or seeming to care about the truth of life at Dannemora. Their reactions were clichés, not the same clichés as those he had grown accustomed to, but dramatic situations which were as false, and were impressive only because they had been done before to good box office.

He was tired. Whose story was this? Certainly not his. Not the prisoners at Dannemora. This picture would do harm, not good.

"Look," the lean man with the hawk's eyes said excitedly, "I got another angle. You had a riot up there, didn't you? Get that! We can bring the riot in—all that stuff—machine guns—tat-tat-tat——"

"That was in 1929," Father Hyland said.

"So what? Who'll know? We can put you in that——"

"That was Father Booth. It wasn't me."

"What difference? It's good stuff."

"They did him already. He's in *The Last Mile*."

"Sure. But it went over, didn't it?"

The bland fat man who ate mints all the time said, "Maybe you got a better angle. What else happened?"

"There was the murder of the band player. Almost the first day I came."

"That's hot. What was it about, a dame?"

"No. About a band instrument."

"No good. Public won't accept that."

"But it happened! It really happened that way."

"Look, Reverend, maybe it did. Now how you going to make anybody believe it? You know that stuff about facts and fiction? See what I mean?"

Hawk-eyes broke in: "We could change it to a dame. Anything else?"

"Yes. There was Lee Sapis Robinson." He told them the story about Lee, which had seemed dramatic enough. Then when he came to the part about suicide, the silent man with the yellow face said, "Nope. Can't use suicide. We'd have the office down on us. And the Legion. Anything else?"

"But this was different."

"Sorry. No can use. What else?"

"There was the building of the church."

"Yes, but I got difficulties about that," the stout man put in. "How's that going to appeal to the Jews and Protestants? Say! How did you get on with the minister and the rabbi?"

"Fine. Just fine. They were back of me right from the start."

"O.K. Suppose we begin with the three of you living together in one house, see? Then we get some romance with the rabbi falls in love with the warden's daughter, like, or something."

"Rabbi Schoenkopf is about sixty. Besides, his wife mightn't like it."

"So what? Make him young. And the warden's daughter is a Christian——"

"Sure," the taciturn man said, "and the padre here marries them in the new church. That's good."

Father Hyland began to feel his reason tottering. "*Abie's Irish Rose*," he muttered. "Look," he said aloud, "we're not getting anywhere. This story is supposed to be about the spiritual rehabilitation of criminals. That's that. And it's that or nothing."

"See?" the fat man interjected again. "That's my trouble.

You took care of the Catholic boys. All right. But what about the others?"

"What others?"

"Protestants—Jews—nothings—who didn't build the church."

"I don't get you."

"The Catholics built the church. O.K. That's fine. But how about those who didn't build it?"

"There weren't any."

The man with the hawk eyes leaned forward. "You mean to say it was built by everybody?"

"Certainly."

"Protestants and Jews?"

"Of course."

"Why didn't you tell us?"

"I simply, honestly, never thought of it before."

"You mean you just took for granted that everybody'd pitch in?"

"Why wouldn't they? It's the same in my office. I don't draw any lines. Why should they?"

"Yeah—yeah—now we're getting some place," the fat man said. "Give us an angle on that."

"Well, all I can think of is—a couple of years ago I had to get altar cards made in three different colors. They're the prayers we stand up on the altar. We take them down every day. And, you see, my man couldn't tell which side which went on, so I had him put the red one on the right side and the green on the left. Otherwise he couldn't tell."

"Why not?"

"Because he was a Jew."

"Boy, oh, boy, that's good for a laugh, yeah."

The silent man grunted. "We'd have to do that in technicolor."

And they spent the rest of the evening discussing the possibility of color versus black and white, which would have the advantage of drabness.

Oh yes. They wanted the picture. But what picture?

He was discouraged and tired as he set out toward Capistrano. He found a rambling inn along the roadside and decided to put up there and go on the rest of the way the next day.

Now, tonight, everything seemed false. He could not sleep and he kept thinking of his parolee who had become a big-time racketeer. He was deeply discouraged.

There was only a week more before the final conference at Culver City and he had to bring all these influential people to a discovery of the realities underneath his own personal drama. How could it be done?

He thought of the beauty of California, but it seemed sham now. The new adobe houses were built yesterday and would fall down tomorrow. The palm trees, left to themselves, were indeed ugly, and only a careful artificiality of pruning kept up their shapeliness. Even the hills were wrong, brown all summer. And there was little remembrance of Fra Junipero Serra in this land.

He must not have delusions. He liked people, places, and it was in his training, as in his nature, to trust everybody and to enjoy everything. Yet he knew what lay down underneath. Funny. Funny, this—to be a priest. To have the secrets of the unmentionable vices of your fellow men locked up in your heart, to be always aware of their surface follies, poses, artificialities, and yet to love them. To know their dishonesties and yet to believe in them. To balance against the fact of original sin the more overpowering fact of God's salvific will.

He got up then. It was hot and stuffy, and he remembered seeing a balcony far down the corridor. Perhaps in the moonlight air he could think things out more clearly.

He kept thinking, "Underneath all men is a beauty, an honesty. In all men is a true thing, a soul. God let me keep remembering that. Let me reach it. Under all folly is a magnificence."

Far down the corridor the moonlight was calm, bright. He could see the citrus groves, the rolling hills, the clipped mountains beyond. Then, suddenly, there was a bulk and a blackness between him and the moon.

Three men. Like something out of the cheapest movie thriller.

"Stick 'em up! Come on, slow, with your hands up. Slow."

The priest, with hands in the air, came slowly toward the moonlight.

"Stand still. Fork over your room key."

As he reached into his dressing gown and held out the key his face must have come into the light.

"My God! It's Pops! Scram!"

As if they had seen a ghost, the three men ran down the corridor, but not before he had seen their faces in the moment of their crime. He remembered the stained-glass windows. Now he had seen them.

2.   Brendon O'Malley could not go back to England. The rains had come in Africa and he felt trapped as once he had felt in Seattle. Everything in him called out for Laura, but the man who had asked his help was a friend and what could he do?

He could cover up the impending scandal only if he stayed here. Besides, he had given his word.

In the beginning, they said there was nothing dishonest about it, but he remembered the conversation in the club and he could not pretend that he had been taken in. He knew. It was crooked. But the disgust had worn off long before he knew his friend was involved.

Personally, he was lily-white. Just covering traces for a buddy, in too deep to turn back. Just being a sap, he supposed. A front guy for crooks. Just a good fellow.

But what else could he do?

3.   On the way to Culver City Father Hyland had been silent, thinking. Away from Dannemora, due to the experiences which he had had, he realized that he had gained a new perspective. But it was not a happy one. How could he convince these men out here, who certainly knew their own business better than he did, that there was a greater story than they

had ever made in the deep fact of the rehabilitation of criminals? He himself was shaken. He was in no mood for the final conference that now was only minutes away.

His mother did her best to distract him, trying to sound like a district attorney. "All right, so you won't talk. Do you want to stew? Or is it fry? I never can remember. It doesn't matter. What's the trouble with you? You're glum as an ox."

"I'm thinking."

"Go ahead, but don't think that way. I've been the damper on this trip so far. Now it's turn about. Ambrose! What are you thinking about?"

"About redemption. I know how to get men going straight. I don't know much about keeping them that way, do I?"

"Your boys go back on you?"

"Maybe society is right. Maybe they're all warped— crooked——"

"You don't believe that."

"Just now I don't know what I believe. That newspaper article——"

"Forget it."

"I can't."

He kept seeing the account that had appeared the day after the holdup.

Priest Routs Parolees. Single-handed, Reverend Ambrose Hyland, chaplain of Clinton Prison, Dannemora, New York, put to flight three armed brigands at the El Rancho Inn. . . . Father Hyland is here to make a picture exposing prison conditions with particular emphasis on abuses in the parole system. His advisors at Culver City state that the clergyman's inside knowledge of prison abuses, such as led to the riot and break of a few years ago . . . It is stated on good authority that before the attempted holdup Father Hyland received several long-distance warnings from well-known gangsters in New York . . .

Hollywood had been enchanted with the publicity. Ambrose Hyland was not.

"Listen," he said finally, putting the journalese phrases out of his mental vision, "there's got to be some kind of group outside that we can educate, so they won't be victims of all this rot. Some organization. There's so much money spent on this nasty propaganda! Now they're using me for it."

"Watch that red light. Don't get up any more plans, Ambrose."

"I have to. We need a group. A foundation. Only that would cost so much."

"Haven't paid for the church yet, have you?"

"No. But this is important."

"Everything is. Take things as they come. Stick this idea in your hat."

"Hat!" he cried. "Hat! Oh yes!"

They had turned right off La Brea Street and all the way he kept telling his mother to watch for a hat store, but they found none until they reached Culver City. Then he had a hard time convincing the salesgirl that he did not care what color or size the hat was, any hat would do, and that she did not need to wrap it.

"What you got there?" his mother asked when he reached the car.

"A hat."

"I see," she said. "That explains everything."

They drove in silence. He made only one wrong turn, and a strange assortment of buildings with no backs, a cement-walled irrigation ditch, and a treeless hill confronted them. A bevy of very unconvincing Indians reined down rapidly, drew up abruptly, and looked bored.

"What's that?" his mother asked.

"A lot."

"I'd say it was a lot of nonsense. They can't be the ones you came to see, Ambrose?"

"No. Mine are a different kind of savage. We'll have to turn back."

Eventually they found the studio, its rows of doors stretching on, chattering people, some in make-up, some in office attire, going in and out. Finally they found a surly attendant.

"You want the exec building. Thataway, around the corner."
Then he saw the two hats. "Oh. You had me fooled. I mistook
you for a real reverend."

"I mistook myself for one until this idiocy," Father Hyland
said.

When at last they reached the office there was an impressive
group waiting for them. A secretary was dancing attendance.

"May I take your hat—your hats—I mean?"

"Oh, this?" Father Hyland realized that he was still carrying
a small gray hat that had, he discovered, an impish red feather
in it.

"Do you always carry two?"

"No. Oh no. This is for a surface vapor-grinding apparatus."

"Oh yes. Of course. Can we do something with it?"

The several men in the office were now completely silent,
looking at him with something like awe.

"Why, yes, you can. You could send it to this address." He
held out a small piece of paper, smiling. "It's for a prisoner."

One of the executives looked as if he were about to make a
note. "Do prisoners wear hats now?"

"No. He's going to cut it up."

Mrs. Hyland intervened. "My son's been through a lot with
you men, and I want you to know that the only thing kept us,
except for running into a horde of Indians, was getting that
hat."

The secretary allowed himself to looked alarmed and pushed
a chair toward Mrs. Hyland. She was undaunted. "I don't
know what Ambrose wants with it. He didn't see fit to tell
me. But if he's sending that hat to one of those poor prisoners,
it's for a good reason. And I want you to know it's more important than any silly old picture. So send it and be done with
it and we can get down to business."

Dismissing the cinema industry with a gesture, she sat down.

His mother's defense of him was perhaps what he had
needed, for when the time came for him to speak, he was
incisive. "Gentlemen, there has been a great deal of misunderstanding about this picture. Naturally, since it's my life, I need

discretionary power over it. But it's not to be about me, or the building of a church, or any fanciful things you may have had in mind. It's about human beings. It's about the man who wanted that hat. That seemed ridiculous to you, didn't it? But to one man, who hasn't anything else, that hat represents an interest, and that means a will to live.

"I don't know how you're going to film that. That's your business. But here's what you must tell people: that men can come back, that some of them don't, but that men can. They can come back only by believing in the dignity of their own creation, and they can't believe that unless they believe that God gave them this dignity, gave them personal lives that are important—at least to God.

"You can't sell that idea unless you've bought it yourselves. You can't tell people what the Church of the Good Thief means unless you've had the courage to look into your own hearts and know your own evil, and your sorrow for it, your repentance, and perhaps, God have mercy on you, your falling into sin again—and again——

"That's not only the story of Dannemora. That's the story of the human race. And it's the only story I'll let you make."

The pent-up emotion of the last days had burst at last, and he sat down shaken, consumed with the solution that had come to him when he had needed it. Why had he doubted? He was asking heroes to believe in redemption despite the fall of man and when he himself had encountered relapse he had not been great enough. But that would never happen again.

Distantly he heard the discussion of terms. Money. There were other more compelling thoughts. Symbols. The church, oranges at Christmas, jobs. The need of a felt hat to use in a machine for grinding tools. A surface vapor-grinding apparatus. Looked like a Rube Goldberg contraption. A couple of round brackets on a stick and an emery wheel and water dripping through it. Cohen couldn't make it come right. He was trying to pad the thing with string. It kept spouting water over him. He needed felt. The felt hat. They all needed so much——

Someone said something about five thousand dollars. He did need money to fight this cause. But much more. Much more.

"Not enough," he said, and his mother told him later that one of the executives had shouted, "You offer a big man like that five thousand dollars to sell his soul! So he faints on you!"

He hadn't fainted, but he did appreciate the glass of water they gave him.

Then he was thinking again. A hat to use in a machine, a sense of importance for today, the knowledge of being needed. Friends outside—heroic friends who would understand repeated failures, recidivists, violators of parole, and the grace of God. A vast, expanding public that would beat down the ignorance of sensationalism——

They were talking terms again. "No. I need much more than that. Much more."

And it was not until they reached the street that the full realization came to him of how much they had finally agreed on. He stopped abruptly.

"Mom!" he cried, taking her by the shoulders, "do you know how much money they're offering me? Do you?"

"Why, yes, Ambrose," she said placidly.

"But, Mom, think what it'll mean! We can really set up a foundation. If nothing else comes out of this, at least we have that. Think of it. *Fifty thousand dollars!*"

She sniffed. "Why, Ambrose," she said, "they've got all kinds of money out here."

CHAPTER FIVE

They had hoped to have the stained-glass windows ready before Father Hyland's return, but imperfect pieces delayed them. They knew it would be spring before they were done.

"At least we have time for craftsmanship," Cyrus Turner had said.

Carlos smiled. "You have taught me a great deal, Maestro."

"Maestro? I haven't heard that in years. I'm just a number here."

"There's a whole town remembers what you did for them during the hurricane. Some people don't forget."

"Is it good not to forget? There's one person we both should forget."

"I have not tried. She is with me always."

"I've got over that. Would you go back to her, even with what you know about her?"

"Yes. Sometime she will know she was wrong. That's all I need."

Turner shook his head. "I'm different. I've been through fear. When you're afraid, your past stands out sharp, defined, like good draftsmanship."

"My fear was a confusion. It was voices screaming at me and whispers in the dark. Then I put my fears on canvas and stained glass. The faces in my dreams went out of me. I have found clarity."

"You'll lose it if you go back to her."

"No. Not now that I know she loves me."

"Loves you?"

"Oh yes. She could not have hated me if she did not love me."

"Carlos," Cyrus Turner said, "I've never loved as you do. You're a very great man, Carlos."

"Maestro!"

Laboriously, Bill Martin kept putting notes down on the music score. He could hear the sounds when he was in his cell but it was hard to get them on paper when people kept coming into the church all the time.

He had hoped to have this ready for the padre's return, but he was not fast enough. If only he knew more about music—composition, harmony, counterpoint. It would need Werrenrath's help, but he wanted to keep this secret. He must tell no one what he was doing.

He was composing a Mass.

Greeney was working on his case.

He had heard, early in October, that there was a lady lawyer who took desperate cases if she knew men were innocent. He was innocent. So that was all right. But how could he know if his letter had gone out? Without Pops's influence you couldn't be sure. He had waited so long. It was December already. Maybe he had the address wrong. Maybe she wouldn't even answer. If Pops would come home he could write her and tell her Allan Green was innocent. Then she'd take the case.

Several times a day Greeney went down to the basement of the church and washed his shirt and pressed his pants. A line of prisoners always waited for the iron, the soap flakes, and the sink. Like him, they were waiting. Washing. Ironing their uniforms. Washing. Ironing. Waiting.

Prisoner 142,465, Andrew Laski, cat burglar, had got a job at last in the carpenter shop where they had a tool grinder. It spat water, but with felt and grease it could be made to work.

"When you getting the felt? String's no good."

"Soon as Pops gets back," Cohen replied.

"How soon that be?"

"I dunno. I can wait."

"So can I."

But it was hard, waiting. Before he could make a boring tool, for which he needed the vapor-grinding apparatus his neighbor had invented, he had smuggled out inch-wide, foot-long pieces of wood which he had buried in the Big Yard. But now he was ready to bore two holes in each, secure some rope, tie them together, and have a ladder.

He was ready, but he needed felt.

He did not know that for several weeks a gray hat was held up because the inspectors did not know why Father Hyland should have sent a hat from Hollywood to Dannemora. It could wait.

Laski was tired waiting.

Bud Horne forwarded the personal mail, opened the general mail, catalogued it, made out replies which would be changed before Father Hyland signed them. Dull, routine, office stuff.

He did not dream about escape the way some men did.

Bud Horne had his own plans, and he wrote down in his notes the hours and minutes of waiting. The days seemed long.

Steve Ploznic was desperate. He needed the padre quick, because if he didn't get the hundred dollars he owed for gambling, they said in the Big Yard, they would kill him.

They meant it.

2. When the chaplain came back to Clinton Prison, he decided that he must never be away so long again. Everything was in confusion. No one had completed anything. As far as he could see, nothing at all had happened while he was away.

3. They talked to Dominic about being in the service but he laughed at them. "I got it good here. What's a difference?"

He got along fine. They kidded him about being the Good Thief but he didn't mind. He had got a job at an airfield in Jersey and at first he thought it would be good if he could do simple jobs. Then he flew, and he wanted to get at the controls. Now he could do double Immelmann, solo.

"I'm too slap-happy to worry," he said.

Yet all the same it might be good to get in the air force. Quite a lot of parolees had won their struggle to be allowed to fight. It made you just like everybody else. And Dominic was used to a lot of people around him all day. Sometimes, though you wouldn't know it, he was lonesome.

He missed Dannemora. He always said he had had a good time there.

4. For a long time now Father Hyland's little cottage had been a rendezvous for the clergy, and since the key was always discoverable, he would never quite know whom he would find

when he returned home. Then lately he had built bunks in his basement for any wandering alumni who might drop in and, though he managed to see most of them, there were some who would help themselves out of the icebox, sleep, and depart without identification.

While he was accustomed to many people, they seemed now to be converging upon him from all sides. Everyone had heard about Hollywood. Even the salesgirl in Plattsburg, from whom he got felt remnants, after he had discovered that a hat curled and was no good, had fluttered and had been clumsy with the string.

"I bet nobody will even look at Clark Gable any more," she said, obviously thinking that the picture was not only to be about him, but that he was to act in it.

He could laugh at that, but he still would go into a fury when stout ladies said with arch-femininity, "Oh, but you love it! You know you do!"

It made him feel as ridiculous as he had that day he went horseback riding. How had he even let himself in for that? Certainly, not because of the ladies who had ridden over from one of the lake resorts and were urging him on as they sat on his front porch. They had insisted, of course.

It had been all very well around the firehouse and the moving-picture theater and not too bad up the hill. Except that he could not remember how to turn around. The horse, apparently, could speak only French, and his French did not extend to horses.

They went far up the mountain. Of his own will, at last, the horse stopped at a watering trough. Ambrose Hyland thought of dismounting, but how would that look? He couldn't lead the horse downhill. He had come for a ride.

Spontaneously the horse turned back. He began to canter, feeling good. His rider felt pretty good, too, until somehow his feet slipped out of the stirrups. He could not find them again.

"Please, God," he prayed, "stop this horse!" He clutched the horse's mane, holding on. The horse did not like that. It made him gallop.

"He'll have to stop somewhere. Horses always find their own barns."

The horse took one look at him over its left shoulder, abandoned the road, careened through the gardens of Dannemora. "Thirty miles an hour," the priest thought. "They can't go faster than that." He pulled at the horse's mane. The horse went faster. There were the big trees in front of his cottage. That would be the end. Concussion. He was certain.

Then the horse leaped a wall. He must have leaped with the horse because he came down still seated. The horse didn't like that. He reared, stood on his hind legs, seemed to walk a few paces, shook himself. His rider went over his head to make a perfect three-point landing.

One of the ladies said, "Such horsemanship! You'll be wonderful in Westerns! You're so *flexible.*"

He did not feel very flexible that night when he tried to crawl into bed after the last of his guests had departed. All his bones were intact, he thought, and if he lay just right . . . No. Not that way.

The doorbell rang sharply. Insistent. Again.

He had trained his alumni to go quietly down to the basement and not to disturb him. Wasn't it late for a front-door guest? The bell again. Something. Must be an escape. An accident.

He pulled his aching body out of bed, slipped into his bathrobe, and went to the door. It was Dominic, grinning widely, ready to embrace him.

"Pops! Surprise!"

"What are you doing here? Come in! How did you get here?"

"I flew."

All absurdities seemed possible, even to Dominic sprouting wings like the Holy House of Loretto. But Dominic explained. "I got a plane. Ain't you glad, huh?"

"No," he said. "I mean yes, of course. Come in out of the light. If they catch you you'll be back inside the gates. You're violating parole."

"I got lonesome," Dominic said simply. "I wanted to see you, Pops."

"That's nice."

"So I took a plane."

"You mean you just picked one up?"

"Aw, I work in an airfield. They'll never miss it."

The phone rang. The priest knew. They had tracked Dominic down. From his bedroom, where he was already dressing, he called out, "I'll drive you to the airport, quick! Get away from here fast as you can!"

"Pops! Have a heart!" The phone rang again.

"I have one. That's the trouble. It can't stand much more."

The chaplain picked up the receiver. When he came back to Dominic, though it hurt him, he was laughing. "Dominic," he said, "we're both wanted."

"Whatsa matter, Pops?"

"In your travels you didn't see a horse, did you? Someone stole one."

"That's bad. They oughtn't steal a horse."

"You're right. But the terrible thing is, I think *I* did."

"I'll cover you, Pops. I got a plane. We can make a getaway."

"No," he said. His head came up. "I'll face the music. But remember, I've been acting very oddly lately. I've been going around with two hats. I've been mistaken for a movie actor. And now, Dominic, let's face the music. I'm a horse thief!"

5. There was a great roaring cry that awakened Brendon O'Malley. He turned over again and tried to sleep. It didn't matter. He was full of quinine and whisky and nothing mattered. Yet he would have to stop them. He was their officer, wasn't he?

Or was he? Which was he doing—celebrating the fact that Laura had had a baby or drowning out a remembrance? He could not quite remember, but it had all been very dignified. He could hear the colonel now.

"There's nothing against you personally, Major. We don't want to investigate."

He felt his back grow rigid. "Is there anything I can do, sir?"

"It would be better all round, old chap, if you resigned your commission."

When the colonel stopped being official and "chappied" you he was dangerous. Of course he had got drunk. And now, hearing the men, he knew they were celebrating because he was no longer in command. He must have resigned already, resigned everything, Laura and the baby——

Thought he was a hero. An ace. Big shot. Through. The men cheering——

Then the orderly said, just as usual, "Your tea, sir."

"I say! Did much of anything happen yesterday?" This was tomorrow, wasn't it? "Did I sign any papers?"

"Nobody did much of anything yesterday, sir. The colonel was a might occupied yesterday."

"What happened? Anything—anything at all?"

"Why, gorblimy, sir, if you don't mind—it was VE-day."

Brendon got up and started to shave.

So. He looked at himself in the mirror, the green face he had never seen before, and prepared to cross over to the colonel's quarters.

So. He had missed the day he had been fighting for. It would always be part of a bad dream.

So.

6.   He could not recall any time when a convict's personal problem had disturbed him more, Ambrose Hyland thought.

"So which is more important," Steve Ploznic had asked, "my life or a hundred dollars?"

The question haunted him as he walked up and down the monastery garden and as he played the organ and as he worked on the plan for the foundation, and in all the places he went for privacy within the gates it came to him. What were his values? Which was more important—a prison regulation or a man's life? There had been real terror in Steve Ploznic.

"I'm not asking you to pay the boys with your own money. All I want is for you to get a hundred bucks from pals of mine. I got to pay my debts. Sure, I shouldn't of gambled. So what? With them after me——"

The priest knew it was so. Men had died for less at Dannemora. There would again be a long gray line, a halt, one man not going on any more. Against that a regulation saying you could not secure money for inmates.

"I'll find a way for you, Steve. Give me a little time."

"How much time? How much time have I got?"

Not much time. The days were shortening all around, for all of them. There was not enough time for anything.

There were other demands, though none so serious as this. Any day now Japan would collapse and then the great needs would arise again. He must be ready and have the Social Service Foundation functioning. But he could not give all his mind to it because of his worry about one man.

He put down his notes and looked out the tower window. Greeney was hoeing in the garden. If Hollywood could see him, he thought, they might just tell the truth, capture one shot of Greeney as he was now, and not send on the atrocious scripts which he had had to reject.

The first had been the best, though it had a subplot which confused itself with the White Sister. Then they had grown progressively worse. The second had turned Dominic into a buffoon and Cassidy into a gangster. It was completely composed of types, "criminal types." And the third thought it was the Big House and at the end of the inevitable riot had killed the chaplain off, heroically dying in a defense of the church.

Oh no. Why couldn't they try to do prison life as it was, inside the hearts of men, even to a portrayal of their faces?

A commotion below had brought this thought, for the men were coming with the stained-glass windows. He had avoided looking at them since he had seen the sketches. Today he and Cyrus Turner would look at them. Turner's last day. But now, before he went down, he would have time for one more interview.

Steve Ploznic? What would he do about him? No. That problem must wait. He must be sure. He would take Jacques, the backwoodsman who had worked at the wrought iron. Good inmate. No major infractions.

He had him brought in and listened to the unhurried recital.

"I just come to tell you my story. I'm a reformed character.

"I was a small boy, three year old once. My mother, she is not a good woman and she goes away, yes, with a man. My father, as with men, goes also with another woman. And us? *Mon père,* there was the aunt, the sister of the mother, and with her own and with us, what could she do?

"I know which way a tree should fall. But school? No. I do not like him. Church? No. Was there one to oppose my stubbornness? And always I am ashamed. The children keep speaking about my mother. Always? That I do not know. Once, twice? To me, always.

"So I run away. When I am in the forests I hear one thing. I will find the mother. So now there are thirty-four years to my age. Every year I come closer. I do not write. I do not read. But I ask. Who have heard of her? One year I get one thing, another year, different. Yet I am closer. So until then.

"For skinning the animals I carry a sharp knife, but I am a prudent man and I do not use it even when I am drunk, even mad like hell. No.

"Still I come closer, and I ask where I find where she live. So I walk up to that house. It has geraniums and a red brick wall. The bricks are turned up with a shape like what? Like the tops of pine trees. Do you know? I think if someone fall down on them, they die. But I do not wish this. Now I am bursting with love.

"I rap on the door. Then she comes. At once I know from the sister of my mother, the mother. I go into the house. She is a frightened woman.

" 'Madame,' I say to her, 'you are my mother.' She say she is not the mother. Thirty-four years are to my age, *mon père.* Can you understand me? I take out my knife when she says she is not the mother and I strike her until she falls down. Do you understand how that can be?

"I do not. I am not sorry, but I go at once to the sheriff. I tell him. Still I am not sorry because when I see those bricks I think it is too bad I had to slice her. She could have fallen by herself there and it would not have been my trouble.

"Twenty-two years, mon père, I have been here because my mother did not die. Now I tell you this truth. At the very last of these years, in your church, I have reformed myself. I have made out of iron, the tabernacle."

Jacques rose and left. He wanted no advice, merely to tell the story, to externalize it, and to be gone. Jacques would feel better now. But once, while he was talking of the knife, Father Hyland had seen in his eyes such an expression as now he must force himself to view, repeated in the stained-glass windows of Dannemora.

CHAPTER SIX

Everybody told Ambrose Hyland that it was dangerous to do what he was doing. He was determined. "Just another occupational hazard," he said.

He looked upon his Roman collar as his best protection. He could go into places where law-abiding citizens were seldom found and emerge unscathed. But if he were to tell others how his men fared, he would have to find them in the holes they crept into after they left Dannemora. They were in strange places, some of them.

This day had begun with the extreme respectability of the Cassidys, to whom he talked whenever the elevated was not passing. Mrs. Cassidy had seen to it that Dan was at his best that night. He wasn't working yet at all, she told the priest, but he would be soon.

"You can't keep a good man down," she said. "I tell him that."

She was so grim about it that the priest knew all was not

well. He winked at Cassidy solemnly, and Big Dan put out his lower lip and turned his mouth down and his forehead up so that there was an understanding about how womenfolk will talk.

When he got Cassidy alone later while Mrs. Cassidy was doing dishes, he heard how it was with them.

"She's a fine woman, Father, but she drives me. She's woise than a roach. I've never been so driven."

"No. You were always a fighter, Dan. You never went soft up there."

"You mean, am I now?"

"How do I know? What happened to the job?"

"I quit."

"I know when you're lying, Dan Cassidy. I always knew. You were fired."

"That's the truth of it. Because some little squirt come trackin' me down, tellin' the men of my record. He got them stirred up and I was through."

The priest's blood boiled. He had met that kind of male spinster before, reformers who carried moral indignation around like a trowel, spading up rotten corpses. Christ Himself had been merciful with sinners, but He had been caustic the day he wrote sins on the sands.

"Good Lord," he shouted over an oncoming train, "did they do that to you, Dan?"

"That's what they did."

"Dan, the years at Dannemora didn't wear you down, so don't let this. And why didn't you let me know?"

"Herself. She's a proud one."

"I see. Listen, Dan, you're going back to that job next Monday. There will be a job to go back to—when I get through with them. Mrs. Cassidy!" he called, and she appeared in the door with her sleeves rolled up. "Get this straight. Your husband is an ex-con. Say that to yourself. Everyone else will be saying it."

"Not while I'm around, they won't."

"It's a fact. So face it. You and Dan are going to get that all

your lives. You've got to learn to take it. Otherwise you'll let
him sit here and get drunk until he's no good. It'll be your
fault. Sure. You love him. You don't want him hurt. But he's
got to be hurt plenty on that job."

"He won't go back there. I'll see him dead first."

"I think you would. Dan! Monday—on the job. Get it?"

"Yeah, Pops. I'll go back."

"And there's one more thing I want to know." He looked
around the room. "Where's your Little Butch?" There was no
Infant of Prague to be seen. "You forgot Him, didn't you? Or
was He too soft for you? You're too big a guy to be dressing
a doll? I remember when you did—when you were a man!"

The priest stalked down five flights and out onto the street.
The taxi driver who tried to ignore him did not have a chance.
The priest was in the back seat shouting a number at him.

His indignation, which he had used to advantage with Cassidy, was really directed at informers. But he must cool off.
No need for high blood pressure at his next stop.

The house before which the taxi drew up with a snarl was
Bill Martin's sister's address. The priest was glad that he
found a light because he had telephoned several times and
received no answer. On the off-chance he had come here.

There was one person at home. It was a boy of about seven-
teen who looked out through the half-opened door and who
had, the priest suspected, surveyed him from the area window
before answering the bell.

"Want something?" he asked.

"Yes. I'd like to see you. I'm Father Hyland from Dannemora."

"Anything wrong?"

"No. I just wanted to see you. You're Eddie."

"Who told you?"

"Your uncle."

"What's he know?"

"Nothing, Eddie."

"All right. Come in."

The aura of fear was in this room. Eddie sat down before

the priest did, his face in shadow, his hands taut on his knees. He would have been a handsome boy with his whipcord body, his sunken eyes set in the perfect oval of his face, had it not been for his tension and terror. Bill Martin had looked this way once.

"How much do you know about your uncle?"

"Plenty."

"Not enough, Eddie. He's very fond of you."

"That's good."

"He only met you once. He talks a lot about you. And you talk about him, I guess. But I don't think you're talking about the fellow I know."

"Maybe not."

"Do you want to hear about him?"

"I don't care."

"He's a great guy. Ed, have you been in service?"

"Not yet."

"He was. They taught him to kill people. He was just a kid —about a year older than you. But he wasn't like you, Eddie. There wasn't anything eating him out." The priest saw the boy's chin jerk up as if he were about to speak, but he went on quickly. "Then he came home. He used to get drunk a little. He went into a tavern with a buddy—a civilian. There wasn't a real fight, just a few words. Bill Martin was trigger-happy and he carried a gun. It wasn't until he heard the shot and saw what was on the floor that Bill knew what he had done."

There was no response, nothing but the tensed hands picked out in a circle of light.

"Now get this. Your uncle wasn't a gangster. He never deliberately hurt anybody. Maybe what he did wasn't a mortal sin. I don't know. God does. But the State thought it was, and Bill Martin has been paying for it with his life." He hoped that the shell would crack, but the boy sat unmoved.

"And you've been paying for it with your life, Eddie. You mustn't."

"Why?"

"Because you don't need to."

"Oh no?" He was silent. "That what you came to say?"

"Yes."

"O.K. You've said it."

"I've done a little more than that. I've taken something away from you. You've had a picture in your mind of Bill Martin the killer. But you'll never have that any more. You'll see a quiet sort of fellow playing the organ in church. He's wearing a black cassock and a white surplice and there are stained-glass windows around him. Look up at one of them and you'll see Bill Martin's face the way it is now. An artist used his face for the dying Christ. Eddie, that's what you'll see of your uncle, Bill Martin."

For the first time the boy relaxed. Thank God, some impression had been made. He seemed to be smiling.

"I knew there'd be something like that."

"Like what?"

"Like what you said."

"What's the matter with it?"

"It's corny."

"Maybe it is. But you believe it. Because it's true." He stood up to go now. Something ached in him toward this lad as though he were his own son. He said finally, "Now I'll tell you something else. Listen to it, Eddie. You don't inherit your uncle's sin. His crime isn't in your blood—it's in your mind."

He did not want to ride over to the West Side; it was raining but he wanted to walk, to keep thinking. They had all sorts of agencies for such lads. They would build up their bodies, sometimes their minds. But where was there a group that could care for the torture of their thinking?

Only his convicts could do that. . . . There was a thought there—something—just back of his mind. But now he had arrived at the address Dominic had given him, in the Italian section just beyond the Village, where Dominic's grandmother lived. He anticipated warmth, companionship, perhaps a glass of chianti, for he knew what Dominic's grandmother must be like.

He was impressed by her rooms, not the bright colors of the

walls nor even the plaques with "Jesus Saves" and "The Lord
Cometh" on them, so much as by their cleanliness. They were
terribly, spotlessly clean from the scrubbed linoleum to the
corrugated ceilings. They smelled clean. Forbiddingly clean.
And the old lady herself looked like a Mediterranean version
of Old Dutch Cleanser.

As quietly as he could the priest began to talk about Dominic, how much he liked him, how friendly he had always been.
And the old lady nodded, as if agreeing with him; then, when
he finished, she said, "Dominic, he bad."

"No, he's not. He's a good boy."

"No. He's-a lost. Me, no. Me saved." She rolled her eyes
heavenward.

"Nobody's lost. Not until they're dead. You know that."

"I know. Jesus saves. He save-a me. But Dominic—no.
He's-a lost."

There was no shaking of her conviction. Eventually he
wormed it out of the old lady that years ago she had joined
some esoteric sect, with which he had only the slightest ac-
quaintance, and was thoroughly convinced of her own salvation and of Dominic's damnation. Though he could not understand her very well he was sure that after she had warmed
to her subject she was making every effort to convert him and
that when he left she was certain that he, too, had gone out
into the night of perdition.

In a way, he had. The time had come to begin his search for
the lost. As usual he went to the wharves. He watched the
workers, fascinated as always by the shining black bodies so
rhythmically hoisting cargoes. Then someone recognized him,
and he was surrounded.

There was a royal welcome for him here, though these were
the fortunates, not the ones he had gone out to find. It was for
those who had been here, who had drifted on, leaving the
smear of their passing like snails, wherever they had been.

In the weird light of the wharves he saw those who had
hung on. How many would survive? Next time some of these
would be sucked back into the whirlpool; other faces would

be here; and after a time they, too, would be gone. Only the hardy could keep at this.

With a guide he began a tour of the water-front saloons. There were so many of them. And as the night wore on he found more of those whom he had come to search out. These were not parolees. These were the ones who had survived the term of parole and now were lustily free to get drunk.

He saw them, talked to them, as they slouched over tables. He tripped over them later, propped up in doorways, sucking red wine out of bottles through their own drool of saliva. Some of them tried him for a touch as they saw his collar and then embraced him and called him "Pops." He found them in dives and flophouses and alleys.

As the dawn came, he felt that he had dreamed them all and he knew that when the fog lifted it would find the streets deserted and clean.

These were the outcasts; these were his people.

At six o'clock he turned eastward and it was almost seven before he reached Saint Mark's Place. Now he wanted a few moments with Bergner and for Max to come and serve his Mass. It would be fresh and wholesome, and what he needed at the moment, reassuring. There were some who were not lost. There could be more. There must be more!

He could not put the recollection of that night out of his imagination. There were the hard, bitter lips, the too-soft, bleary eyes; there were the loud and belligerent, the self-pitying and the weak. There were the lily-of-the-valley-scented young men with soft white hands; and there were the old, callous in body and soul. But he knew, he knew there must be a way.

The early-morning fog had lifted now and people were emerging for the day's work—people who did not know the night. But he saw them all with a new sight, as if there were something desperate beneath their hurry. The whole world needed an awakening. It needed the honesty of fear.

For a moment he was back again on the Top of the Mark, not as he had seen the city that night, dangerous and repulsive under the beauty of the lights, but as something for which he had compassion. All men, the caught and the uncaught, punished and free, down there under the lights of all the cities of the world. Sounds of haste, covering of laughter, could not reach up so far.

"O God," he prayed, "give them the gift of fear!" And then, though he did not know it, the small atom was split to a dread that the world would never again be without.

He knocked at Max Bergner's door. He knocked again. A slatternly woman put her head out.

"I'm looking for Mr. Bergner."

"He's left. Don't know where. He didn't leave no address." She shut the door.

He walked up to Saint Patrick's Cathedral because he wanted to. It was nine-thirty before he reached there and the sun was high.

He said Mass in the Lady Chapel and a great grace came to him, for he knew then that the men who had seen him that night had found, in his sight, a memory. Even in their stupor they had seen a church which they had built rising upon a hill, over the barred dungeons, over the terrible walls, towering even over the gates of Dannemora. For a moment they had remembered, and who but God knew what their last memory might be before the judgment? He kissed his amice and was glad.

Yet each time he turned for the *Dominus vobiscum* he was troubled by the sight of a young man kneeling there, with the look of eagles, with flaming hair, with a drawn, starved face, contorted, upraised, praying, not as Catholics do, but desperately. Praying against some hideous thing within him. He could feel the intensity behind it, and he realized that even during Mass in that cathedral there was a lurking evil and an impending wickedness. There came an awareness of his own unworthiness which the priest had never felt before. *"Domine, non sum dignus."*

And in Brendon O'Malley's mind there was the refrain,

"God, don't let me do it." And in back of it was the memory of weeks of hunger while Laura and he and the baby had lived in a luxurious apartment, keeping up a front; days when he had stolen milk; times when there had been promise but no fulfillment; hours of threat; never giving in. And now this chance.

"God, don't let me meet him this noon! Don't let him come! Don't let me do it."

Through the petition, through the stirring sight of the priest's face as he turned, haggard and tired, for the blessing, through all was the certainty that he would do it. The man would come. He had the knowledge, positive, that these were words he was saying, and below the words, the plans maturing in some cavernous place under his mind, underneath his prayer.

CHAPTER SEVEN

They all had to take care of him. He wouldn't eat if you didn't feed him. It wasn't that he was worried about something, though they knew that also, but just that he would get so engrossed in his prayer or his work that he would forget about meals.

In the lavatory off the inner office, now also bright with inset stained glass, the coffee was percolating and the two strips of bacon and the fried egg were ready for Father Hyland's breakfast. Greeney had brought a pitcher of canned orange juice to the sacristy for Pops to drink after Mass.

If he dawdled too long over his thanksgiving, Bill Martin was prepared to arouse him with full organ; if he stopped to read his mail while the eggs hardened, Carlos would sit on the rest of the correspondence. The priest would go into the inner office then, and probably take time for breakfast. God knows whether he ate or not when he was out from under the surveillance of his guardians.

But this morning, Bud Horne thought, he had better be on

time. The two black bags were crammed with the usual mail, packages carefully hidden under the boxes of Saint Dismas medals that had just arrived. The chaplain had been pleased with them. What was it he had said? "Remember what Dempster MacMurphy said years ago? That Saint Dismas was the forgotten saint. He had no church, no painting, no medals, no statue to him. Now he has most of those things, and some-day he will have his statue too."

He had been so delighted. It was just as well, Bud Horne reflected, that he had something to be delighted about. He didn't know what was coming. Just suspected trouble brewing. But Bud knew. It had been his plan.

He did not hate Father Hyland. But he remembered all the men whom he had seen going out the gates, while he himself had waited, without help. He remembered, too, the men who had been trusted, and the padre had never believed in him. But now the chaplain had better be careful. He might think he bore a charmed life, but nobody did, when the gang was out to get you. They had got Father Booth, hadn't they? They could get Father Hyland too.

Bud was safe. He'd be out of here. Finally. This was his last day.

He put the egg on a plate when he heard the commotion on the iron stairs and watched the grease harden while Father Hyland riffled through the mail. Then followed the usual process—Carlos brushing off the priest's cloak, which always got whitened by the flaking tower wall, until it had become a ritual to dust him at the top and the bottom of the stairs. Now that was done. For a change he came in, bringing only two letters with him. Greeney followed with a parcel marked "Fragile." Rapidly the priest tore off the covers, spilling ex-celsior onto the carpet. "Vacuum sweeper," Bud Horne re-minded himself. Efficient to the last. That was the game.

"Look! Isn't this grand!" The priest was lifting cups out of the box, cups as big as shaving mugs, and each one had in bright, flaking gold letters "Pops" written across it. Without pausing he started to pour coffee into one.

Bud intervened. "Wait a minute. I'll wash that." He had to watch out for everything. He wondered who would do these things when he was gone.

"They're from Dominic! Isn't that grand?" You would think somebody had given him a million dollars. The padre had always liked Dominic. Right from the beginning. He had worked hard enough to get him a job.

"I wish he had put his address on these. Anybody know where he is?"

"Marines," Bud Horne answered. "Flight. Just back from the East but he got there after the shooting. Now he's at Pendleton."

The chaplain hesitated for a moment. He knew that Dominic had been decorated for bravery at Iwo. No. He would not defend Dominic on Bud Horne's last day. What was the use? He slit open an envelope.

"Hello! What's this?" The spidery, Germanic handwriting was familiar. "This is a day! Bergner made it! He's in a Carthusian monastery in Switzerland. That's wonderful, isn't it? No. That's too bad."

"Make up your mind," Bud Horne said. "What's too bad?"

"It's a shame he couldn't find a religious order in America to take him. There ought to be a place for men when they get out. You never thought of being a monk, did you, Bud?"

"No."

"I thought not." He smiled and grew serious quickly. Clutching the unopened letter, pushing away the rest of his breakfast, to Bud Horne's disgust, he hurried down to the church and knelt there for a long time.

Suddenly he had seen the way. There were many men here who had served a postulancy for religious life and who wanted to be brothers. There would have to be a religious order for penitents, not only for men like Bergner, who was exceptional, but for the less advanced souls. An active life such as they were used to. A long postulancy. Adequate novitiate. A probation period, and then?

Then they could be placed as janitors and secretaries in

parish churches. Invaluable assistants in the C.Y.O. work. More! A real house of reformation, not a reformatory, where old thieves could teach young thieves how to steal heaven. Dismas!

Eddie. Bill Martin's nephew. Admiring gangsters. All the lads in America who were growing up to admire gangsters. The outburst of juvenile crime. Who else could influence them differently, except his own men? The Sisters of the Good Shepherd had done tremendous good for girls. They had their Magdalenes. He must have something like that for men.

Another thing. Who would know how to care for those old derelicts he had found in New York? There had been no social security for them in prison and the charity homes were full of the deserving. These men, conditioned to regimentation, could not adapt themselves to a life outside. And who cared? You could put a dog in a pound, but these were abandoned human beings.

Kneeling before the Blessed Sacrament wrapped in this kind of thinking in the presence of God, which he knew to be true prayer, it all seemed so clear. All the thoughts of the past years fitted into place.

He did not need much. He had so much already. A carefully selected band of ex-prisoners, trained as they were here to love the liturgy, to pray, to lead almost monastic lives. The foundation was already established. It could become a third order, and there would be his answer to the problem about men devoted to the task of reclaiming prisoners, as the Trinitarians had done, but now using modern means, getting jobs for parolees. Vowed under God to continue this work even though they discovered ingrates and recidivists and men just weak like themselves. Trained on the lesson of the healing of the ten lepers, only one of whom came back to say "Thank you."

All he needed was one bishop to approve, and a piece of land. That was all.

Then a wave of shame came over him. Who was he to be thinking of himself as the founder of a great religious order? Founders were all saints, and surely he was not one. Sometime ago a Western archbishop had asked him to help found a new organization to care for stray shepherds and he had written, very honestly, "I would feel better to come as an inmate. I cannot come as a founder." Now what was he thinking of?

He was not good enough. God could not possibly be choosing him. But somewhere, somehow, God must find some holy man to begin this work because it was so searingly necessary. He himself could do the spadework. It was not like building a church. Anybody could do that. But this took sanctity, and God knows he was no saint.

That was not what Carlos thought when he saw him kneeling there. Others might have seen him in Hollywood or riding a horse or dining at Joe Madden's but his church gang had seen him very often at prayer. They measured a man differently when he was on his knees.

Carlos hated to interrupt, but it was necessary.

"Pops," he whispered, "the warden wants to see you."

This was unusual. Not since Warden Synder's time had he been sent for.

He rose, and when he reached the hall he asked, "Do you know why?"

"Something about Steve Ploznic. He wants to know about him, I guess. At least he said to bring your notes on him along."

Oh yes. He knew that case well enough. He remembered when he could think of little else.

It was just after he had come back from Hollywood. That movie. It had certainly taken his mind off it—thinking about the threat from the Big Yard to kill Steve if he didn't pay up the gambling debts. Mortal terror. He remembered how he had suggested that he get Steve a job as cook in segregation, where he would be shut away from those who threatened him. He remembered the debate that he had had within himself about violating the prison regulations, getting the hundred dollars, saving a life. A guard had spoken to him about the case, and he remembered wondering one day soon after what

Steve had meant when he had said, "Thanks, Pops," and refused to explain further, except to say that the threat was over. He realized, of course, that somehow Steve had got the money, and he was glad. Now what could the warden want to know?

Hastily he climbed the iron stairs and called out to Bud Horne, "The warden wants me. I'll say good-by when I get back. Give me the notes on Steve Ploznic." He was surprised that even with Bud's usual efficiency the notes could be produced so quickly. It was as if they were ready for him. As if Bud had expected this.

And Bud Horne would not say good-by then or later, because he was sure that before the chaplain got back he himself would be on his way to Plattsburg. For a while he watched the priest going downhill, cutting across the carefully tended lawn where no one else would dare to step.

"He doesn't know what he's letting himself in for," he thought. If this didn't get him, the next thing would. One after the other. Pile them up. That's the way they had got Padre Booth.

Bud Horne hated nobody. He just wanted people to realize what he had gone through. And he knew how to make them realize it.

2. Through the almost empty courtroom a lone reporter would wander now and then, make a note, and depart. The case of the State vs. Brendon O'Malley had no new angles since the first sensational break. There probably would be nothing new until the judge handed down the verdict.

It had looked promising at first. The angle about the American flier who married above his station, had as much money as he needed while in service, then landing stone broke in New York and trying to keep up a big front because of his wife, had been good copy. The human-interest angle on his mother had been good too. A nurse, working all her life, to educate this fellow. He never had had to worry while she was around.

But now it was just like a hundred other stories about a spoiled kid who had got too quick promotions in the war. There were too many of them. The public was pretty well tired of hearing about the crack-ups of heroes.

And there was no doubt about what the verdict would be. No suspense. Looking into everything O'Malley had done in Spain and England and Africa was just so much legal claptrap. He had been caught red-handed with the jewels in his pocket. He had a large check with him. The jewels had been flown in illegally. Maybe he didn't smuggle them in personally. Who cared? He had them and he had been paid by the combine.

Of course he hadn't been eating very well lately and the Sutton Place rent had been overdue, but why couldn't he get an honest job like anybody else?

There was no use wasting time or sympathy over a fellow like that. It wasn't even news any more. There were too many ex-officers.

This kind of thing would take them down a peg. They needed it.

3. Ever afterward Ambrose Hyland was to remember that interview as the end of one phase and the beginning of another. He had suspected that something was afoot, but now he knew. Father Booth had experienced this years ago. Now it had come to him.

He was ready for it. He remembered Joe Hogan's warning, and he knew from the beginning of the interview with the warden that the time had come.

"Of course," the warden said, "I merely want your denial, Father. Personally I am quite aware that there's no foundation for this rumor at all. Just some misunderstanding. I'm positive you can clear it up."

"I'll be glad to. What do they say?"

"I hope you don't mind. I had to look into it, of course. It seems here that some people have the idea you've been helping a prisoner out with money. Of course, in your position, you want to help in any way you can, but it is against regulations——"

"Sir, there's no need to try to find excuses for something I didn't do. I wanted to. But I didn't."

"Now don't worry about this——"

"I'm not worried."

"That's good. You see, it's rather a clumsy affair. They say here that you persuaded a guard to get money for this prisoner —Ploznic."

"That's quite inaccurate. A guard mentioned the case to me. That's all."

"Oh? Then the accusation is not quite without foundation. It says here that the inmate received the money from the guard and that the guard—now mind you, this is just an allegation—had this idea on your advice. We know that the prisoner received the money."

"How do you know that?"

"I'll be frank with you. Because it was marked. It did come from the guard. But as far as your part in it goes, I'll just accept your unsubstantiated denial, unless, of course, unless——"

"Unless I have an explanation? I see. And if I haven't any?"

"Why, we won't push charges. Fortunately, the witness to your negotiations with the guard is no longer with us. In fact, I believe he has just left. Just this morning."

"I see. You think you're covering up for me. You also accept the word of an inmate over mine. I quite understand. You really have taken Bud Horne's statement——"

"Please. No names. I have confidences like yourself. And all I needed was your complete denial. I have that. That's all there is to it."

"Are you sure?" he asked, rising. "Isn't there anything else?"

"No. Nothing serious. No."

"That means there is something."

"Oh, just the usual things. Some people think you've been a little unwise to spend so much time with what you call your alumni. You know what such contacts with the underworld usually mean—not in your case, of course, but there are so many rackets and it's so easy to use an unsuspecting person——"

"I am never unsuspecting."

"I don't suppose you are. Still, there are some rumors about you housing parolees in your cellar. I suppose that's largely fiction, but you can't be too careful."

The only parolee he could remember, he had turned out very summarily. Dominic. The other men who had come to him had been off parole, free.

"And," the warden went on, "that's about all. Nothing to get alarmed about."

No. Nothing, the priest thought, as he left the office. Nothing except that his old, free life was over. He would not change, of course, but there would always be the feeling that he was being watched, his actions commented upon. He remembered hearing that Father Booth had been followed. That was absurd, but he knew now how it would feel.

He was glad, when he climbed back to the church, that Bud Horne had gone. He could not see him now, though he had been the perfect secretary for so many years. Nobody could replace him. But why had Bud turned against him? He could recall giving him nothing but kindness. Even against his better judgment, at the end he had secured Bud's release. He had not told him that.

No one was in the office when he got there. Eleven thirty-five. The men had gone to their cells at eleven-twenty to prepare for lunch. He would have time to open the letter which he had carried about with him all morning. He tore it open.

Mr. and Mrs. Cyrus Turner request the pleasure of the company of The Reverend Ambrose Hyland at the formal unveiling of a new statue by Mr. Turner.

He whistled. Mr. and Mrs. Turner. He wondered whom Turner had married. He wondered if Carlos knew.

But he had no time to ask him. A messenger came in with

an official memorandum signed by the principal keeper. It was for a transfer, a "boat" as they called it, for Sing Sing. Carlos's name led the list, and as the chaplain read down he realized what it meant. Every one of his crew except Greeney and Bill Martin was on the draft. Almost a clean sweep.

His old church gang was gone.

He knew why.

4.   From the beginning Brendon O'Malley had known that the verdict would be guilty. He had known what would happen from that first warning he had had in Africa, where nothing drastic had been done to him. But then he had felt heroic, covering the tracks for a friend, not personally involved.

At first he had made a clean break with all that, when he had come to New York with Laura. No one could understand about their life there, and people would think he had squandered money and lived beyond his means. That had not been so. There had always been a chance for something big, and Laura had said that their address was an investment.

Of course he could not fly again, after resigning his commission, but there were other opportunities, always close, always for top men who lived at good addresses. There was nothing for people who slipped.

If it weren't for the whispers about him, he might have got something good. If people had left him alone! Why did they bother him? He didn't bother them, did he? He tried to fight down the impression that he was being spied upon, talked about, even plotted against. It was absurd.

Why should they be interested in him? Them? Who were *they*?

It was at this stage of his thinking that he began to be uncomfortable with his own and Laura's acquaintances. He felt at ease only when he was at home with Laura and the baby or with the two or three men who knew about his African experiences and had themselves been involved in getting gems into America. He could relax with them. They knew.

But outside of them there were only suspicions. Suspicions

all around. Enough to keep him from getting a job. The kind of job he needed to support Laura. She had said that she was willing to go to work at Bloomingdale's if she had to, but that must not happen. Mustn't.

Then what? It was not quite clear to him. Despite what the men had said he had known that it was wrong to do what they asked, and that it would be fatal. This he had known with absolute clarity. He had gone to Saint Patrick's that day and prayed there because it was Laura's church and because he had thought that if he held the memory of her kneeling there praying, he might be moved more strongly. Yet he had known before he had gone in that his mind had been made up.

When do you come to a decision? Where was the conscious place where you say yes? Or was there ever such a choice? He could remember the time when he had been thinking about the possibility. That was when they had told him that all he would have to do was to accept a small package from a former flier whom he knew and pass it on to a jeweler whom he also knew.

He remembered rejecting the plea that as he was already in this so deep he might as well get some profit out of it. He recalled avoiding these people for several weeks. And then, how did that happen? He looked them up.

All this was quite clear. And the time, much later, when he realized that he would do it, was quite clear. Between there never had been a moment when he had said, "I will do it." Just the certainty that somewhere in that interval he had made up his mind.

So he had done it. And he had not even been surprised when the hand was on his arm, and he knew it was the law. That, too, he had known. From the beginning that he was being used. It was no surprise.

He had done it. It was wrong. He had known what he was doing. There was only the legal declaration left, the verdict.

It was "Guilty." Of course.

He did not think of himself. He looked for Laura and his mother.

They, too, were as he had expected them to be. Laura lifted her head high. "Chin up!" she was saying to him. His mother's expression did not change at all. Throughout the entire trial her eyes had been sending the constant message to him.

"Brandon, I loved your father. I always understood. It didn't matter what he did. And I love you."

5. No one ever escaped from Clinton Prison, Dannemora.

Andrew Laski knew that he would. He had been patient. For two years. He had made his own tools, sharpening a piece of steel on the water-vacuum machine. He had made an awl. Bit by bit he had accumulated nuts and screws. Over the months he had bored holes at each end of his carefully constructed ladder. He had made a kind of chisel, small but sharp, and every night he had removed an imperceptible amount of cement from around the stone blocks in his cell, carrying away the dust in his shoes every morning. Then he collected the rope.

The real danger had come in the last few weeks, digging up the boards in the Big Yard and having them in readiness, lightly covered over with sand. There had been the chance that someone would find them. Nobody did. So he was ready.

When the night came he removed the stone slab, crept through the opening, swung himself out to the dangling hose, clambered to the top of the tier. It was easy to get to the roof, to crouch along, shadowed by the abutments until he came to the hospital pavilion, a broad open space where patients sunned themselves. There was a spot here where the shadow of the steeple of the church was a black protection against the searchlights. Climbing buildings had been his profession, and he had faced harder obstacles than this. He was down.

Then came the fence to the Big Yard. He scarcely felt the few gouges that the barbed wire gave him as he vaulted over. He dug up his timbers and fastened them into a ladder, bolting the improvised grappling hooks.

Between flashes of the search beam he crept, inch by inch, behind tables and garden hummocks, an hour of crawling, until at last he reached the wall. Then, between flashes, the ladder was up. A moment's wait. He was up, lying flat while the beams played around. The ladder was pulled up beside him. Another wait. The lowered ladder, the beam of light, the darkness, and he was down the ladder.

When the ladder broke, he fell about ten feet, not more. His ankle was twisted but the pain meant nothing and he could run, now he was free.

Andrew Laski ran, and a wall loomed up before him. He turned and ran. Again and again. On four sides of him were walls. There were gates in the walls, tremendous and barred. Still he ran. Gates. Gates.

His ankle shot flame into him. The cuts from the barbed wire, unfelt until now, stung like whips. Until his palms were bloody he tugged at the broken ladder but he could not loosen it from the wall where it hung, the grappling hooks clinging fast.

He ran until he fell. When morning came they found him lying there, clutching at the gates, within the outer enclosure.

No one ever escaped from Clinton Prison, Dannemora.

6. There was a great stir in the prison population that morning in 1947. Last night's attempt at escape would have amused them, but today they would learn whether four hundred of them would have their terms shortened. The new penal code had been established, shortening the time mandatory for many crimes. This affected new prisoners, but Senator Mahoney had a bill pending, asking that the code be retroactive, to include the older offenders. It meant years off their sentences. This noon they would know.

The new man, Knocko Peters, had ambled up to Bill Martin the day before.

"D'ya think Pops'll be home tomorrow?"

"No. He's away in the Catskills. I think it's about that movie."

"I thought that was dead."

"I guess it is, but Pops won't give up. You know how he is."

"Yeah. I guess that's all. I guess I can't ask him a little favor."

"Anything I can do?"

"I don't want to get you into no trouble."

"Quit stalling. What gives?"

"I was going to ask if maybe we got news tomorrow that Dewey signs the bill, you could give us a tune on the chimes— sort of to celebrate."

Bill Martin smiled. "I don't see anything wrong with that, do you? And I'd feel like celebrating. I'm fifty to life, but suppose they cut it down to thirty. I'd only be fifty years old instead of seventy." Then he thought. "Hell," he said, "how you know if Dewey signs?"

"I got ways. I'll tell you, kid. It's coming through Bud Horne. He's a big shot. He's got a paid commercial on the radio. I'll know at twelve. Then if you play then, we're O.K. If you don't, it means no soap."

"Boy, will I play those chimes!"

The arrangements sounded a little farfetched and probably Knocko was lying about the signal on the radio. May have been a buildup for himself, and the chances all were that he would get the information from the trusties who would be working outside and would return for noon chow. But Bill didn't care. If it were information, he would certainly relay it, sounding out the glad tidings on the carillon.

"All set?" Knocko went on. "You got it straight?"

"I got it straight. Who wouldn't? And don't worry, we'll get it, and I'll play."

But at noon that day the carillon did not ring from the tower of the Church of the Good Thief. Governor Dewey had vetoed the bill.

At one o'clock, when the guards came to release the men from their cells to work, none would move.

Four hundred of the older offenders at Clinton Prison, Dannemora, were on strike.

CHAPTER EIGHT

The chaplain had not gone to see about the movie, though it was no wonder that Bill Martin had thought that that was his purpose. He had gone so many places about it, seen so many people. Three years had passed since he had received the telephone call from Hollywood. Now the Independents wanted it. He did not care who did it; but it must be done. People were saying, "Isn't it too bad they never made that picture of yours?" He was tired of explaining that it was still not a dead issue.

He kept telling himself that even Hollywood could not discard such vast sums as they had already expended. But money went so fast. His own fifty thousand dollars had nearly disappeared. There had been so many calls on him.

Today he must not think about that. He must find Cyrus Turner and his new wife. At Woodstock he had been told to turn off right on a woods road marked "Hayloft Theater" and to ask there. You couldn't miss it, they told him.

He did miss it two or three times. But at last he came out into a clearing and found an extraordinary building, open on the sides to wind and weather, which, from the playbills, was the theater. The building was deserted. The sloping floor was, as far as he could see, firm-packed earth, and the benches were rough slabs over sawhorses. What people wouldn't go through for summer theater, he thought. Poor Turner. Lost in this wilderness.

"Hello!" he called out to emptiness. Gingerly he picked his way across a cluttered stage to the door. He called out again, and a girl who had been working on a canvas set piece down beneath the birches stood up hastily. Her red hair straggled loose from a bandanna and her blue denim coveralls were hitched with twine.

"Want something?" she called hoarsely.

"Cyrus Turner! He lives in a red barn." As he approached her there was an unmistakable odor of fish glue.

The girl pushed away a disordered lock of hair and implanted a heavy dirt smudge on her nose. "Phew," she said. "Sizing. I stink." She unloosened the bandanna, letting free a torrent of bronze. On closer inspection she seemed to be quite an unusual girl, not unattractive in a sort of carven way with her high cheekbones and wide nostrils. Her face was somehow familiar.

"I'm just through. Can you give me a lift to Cy's? I ought to know the way." She laughed. Her voice was curiously uninflected, almost a monotone, but she had an odd gift of emphasis that pointed every line.

"You work here?" the priest asked.

"Off and on." She ran ahead of him to the car and was in before him. "Turn right at the apples. Follow the ruts until you get to the bridge. I'll tell you then. Everybody's going to Cy's today."

"You know Cy pretty well?" he asked, making conversation.

"Fairly. Turn left here and up the hill. Now an abrupt left through that field. There's the barn. Did you know him when?"

"Yes, very well."

"Then I know who you are. Cy will be glad. See those cars?"

The cars certainly must have come through some other road, Father Hyland thought. There were a great many of them clustered around the red barn.

"How did they ever get here?"

"Same way they get to the theater. If it's good, they'll come. Pull up way around that side, will you? Cy's the sensation this season. I don't want to mill through that crowd. I've got to wash my face. Golly, I stink."

There was no denying the odor of glue. It clung to the car even after the girl had jumped out. She called back to him, "I'm Mona Turner. I'll send Cy down."

No wonder she had seemed familiar. He had seen her picture so often.

While he was waiting, Father Hyland listened to the conversations around him. Obviously Turner was the discovery of the year. Suddenly, he became aware, people had remembered him again. The prison term and its occasion were reduced to a romantic episode.

In this world, the priest thought, it is possible. Hollywood. The theater. The world of art. Under its tawdry surface there was a charity. A man was not judged by past misdeeds but by present accomplishment. It was better than the bourgeois persecution of the trades.

When he saw Cyrus Turner he knew that everything was well, "Padre," he called. "Pops! Let's get away from this angry mob. I want to talk to you."

His exuberance was so great that even the devoted admirers dared not intrude on this meeting. He took the priest out into the pasture, asking about the men he knew, telling of his own triumphs, and ending with, "But this is the day. I knew you would come."

They were far enough away from the crowd so that the priest could ask the question uppermost in his mind. But he was reticent. In a way this was a new Turner, whom he did not know very well, confident, sure. Sometime he would have to remind him of the Sacred Heart with the tremendous hands. Now there were other things.

"I met your wife," he said at last.

"She told me. That's grand. She's a great girl, isn't she? Does great work."

"What else does she do, besides making scenery?"

Turner bellowed with delight. "You don't know? Why, man, she's the best actress up here. Set for Broadway any time. And does she know it!"

"But wasn't she sizing scenery when I saw her?"

"Sure. They all do. That's part of summer stock. Anything for *theater*."

"I see. You've got something. Something big." He was

thinking of values, people working for a cause, no matter what they did. It was good.

"I suppose you're wondering about Mona," Turner said more slowly. "You wouldn't believe what I found out. She was jealous of me—even of poor Carlos. That was when she thought she could paint. Not now. She knows she can act. As long as people can do something they're all right. Myself, I was a rotten musician. It hurt me."

"But," the priest was still baffled, "the way you felt about her——"

"You softened my thinking a bit, remember?" Turner's whole manner had changed. Here was the real man again. "Look, Pops. You have never known what you've done. Never even suspected. I'm an example—just one. I came out of Dannemora still bitter. Still, I wanted people to believe in me. Oh, I knew I was pretty rotten, but I wanted somebody to trust me more than I trusted myself. You were the only one, Pops." He paused and smiled reminiscently. "You didn't have to trust me. You just did. And when I came out I was looking for someone who would believe in me too."

"And Mona did?"

"No. It didn't work out that way. One day I woke up. I discovered I was asking for something I had never given in my life. I had never believed in somebody else the way you had believed in me. Then how could I ask for belief? So I began to think about Mona. I knew all there was to know about her, but you had known about me, and if you could do it, I could. I wrote her then. She wrote back."

"I'm glad," the priest said. "I'm glad it was that way."

"So—thanks, Pops."

"And—and what about Carlos?"

"Carlos is a great man, Padre. But, you see, Mona didn't need Carlos. She needed me."

Together then they walked back to the barn, where Mona, radiant and well-groomed, had gathered the spectators into the studio. At the end of the loft was a podium where a huge sheeted block of marble stood. Cyrus Turner walked up to it and began to speak.

"Friends, thanks for coming. I want you all to see something I've done. I have lived with it and worked on it for two years. I'm going to miss it. But I will always see it where it is going to stand. God knows I should. I am giving this back to the man who gave everything—when I was a convict at Clinton Prison, Dannemora."

He pulled the cord, and hanging from the cross to which he was tied with rope, hung the majestic figure of Dominic.

It was Saint Dismas. It was Dominic. Not the Dominic that Carlos had painted over the altar with his look of pained surprise, but a majestic figure that had already heard the words of regeneration. It was a criminal face, its lines strong as the evil faces of the stained glass, but one which at that moment had been transformed into terrifying beauty. It was Dismas.

Around him the priest could hear the murmurs, the technical tongue of art. But for himself, not caring whether he was a Philistine or not, he saw only the meaning, the triumph of love over bitterness, the instant straightening of a warped soul, the miracle, the grace.

It was Cyrus Turner. It was Dominic. It was all the world. It was Saint Dismas.

2. Bill Martin scribbled the notes down fiercely. For three years, more, he had been working on his Mass—the Mass he had thought would be done before Father Hyland came back from Hollywood. That was a laugh. The Hollywood offer still hung fire; the Mass remained unfinished. But he had been learning. Studying hard. Now he knew the things he had needed.

He had worked with Father Coakley of Pittsburgh, with Dr. Bennett of the Liturgical School of Chant. In a correspondence course which Pops had arranged for him his average had been ninety-five. He would be a graduate student, except that he was not allowed to go to Toledo for the final seminar. But he had mastered his technique—done all in his power

to make himself a musician, and still the Agnus Dei would
not come. Until today. Now he had it.

"Lamb of God—who takest away the sins of the world—
have mercy on us."

The music had never said what the words said to him until
today. But now, now—— It had taken this thing.

A clipping from the New York *Dispatch:*

FIRE ARMS UNEARTHED IN PAROLEE'S CELLAR

Kingston, N.Y. A well-stocked arsenal was discovered early this
morning by federal investigators in the cellar of John "Bud"
Horne, who together with three other men is being held without
bail.

Horne, released sometime ago from Clinton Prison, Dannemora,
on the request of the prison chaplain, Reverend Ambrose Hyland,
had, as an inmate, been largely instrumental in the construction of
the Church of the Good Thief on prison property.

Horne is believed to have been reunited with his previous gang
shortly after being released on parole. In his possession were found
sawed-off shotguns, sub-machine guns, and approximately twenty
revolvers, concealed under the cellar flooring.

Investigations leading to the arrest were begun after the capture
and conviction of a nineteen-year-old youth for armed robbery with
intent to kill. The youth is a nephew of one of Horne's previous
cellmates and collaborators on the Church of the Good Thief at
Clinton Prison.

Police officials here deny that there is any connection between
Horne and the Brink robberies in Boston, but unofficial sources
maintain . . .

It had taken this thing.

The notes came feverishly. *Miserere nobis*—have mercy on
us.

Father Hyland had said that crime was not hereditary. Sin
could not be passed on from generation to generation. It was
wrong of Bill even to think that about his nephew. The priest
had talked to the boy.

What did you pass on? Why were there whole families that seemed condemned to the repeated pattern of evil? Tendencies. Disposition. Thinking. Not only environment. Bill Martin had met his nephew only once. The latent superstition still lurked in the mind that this thing ran in the blood. People saying, "I know. You could not help it. Your family was the same."

Oh no. The world must change its mind, not set a trap like that for the innocent. Why didn't it leave people alone? What was this business about leading an independent life? Who did?

So they had got Eddie. Armed robbery, assault, intent to kill.

My uncle . . . my uncle . . . at Dannemora . . . my uncle who killed a man!

"Agnus Dei!" He heard the fierce cry and captured the sound that was loud all around him.

"Lamb of God, who takest away the sins of the world, have mercy on us!

"Lamb of God, who takest away the sins of the world, grant us peace!"

3. It was a great roaring sound. Carlos Santa Cruz heard it. Like nothing he had ever experienced before.

He had thought that he had been happy when he had seen his Saint Dismas hanging over the great altar of the church. He had even been happy when he had come here to Sing Sing and the Good Thief Foundation had established a school of stained glass and it had sent men, instructed by him, out into the world, prepared to make beauty. Maybe that had been happiness. This was joy.

Joy is an aching, a sudden, bursting thing. It is tears and a wild cry. It is a too quick lifting of an intolerable burden which you think you have placidly borne.

No one had warned him. He had gone before the board shaking, not knowing what was wanted of him. No one had said anything and he had not been prepared.

This was too soon. The years had not been enough. He was not ready yet.

If somebody had told him. The padre had been working all the time, helping, unknown, to establish the school; and now there was a place which he had secured for him, with his own workshop, his own students, the great craftsmen of the world vouching for him and taking him into their ranks.

"Pops," he had whispered at first.

But now freedom was a clash of wings in the air and a great sounding in the atmosphere. Freedom was a music. Freedom was like love!

He shouted along with the tremendous roaring that he heard all about him.

"Now I will find Mona!"

4. There was only one thing he could think about now, Father Hyland realized, after he had returned from Woodstock. Matters had crowded up tremendously, he knew, but nothing else mattered except this.

It was a letter from the Marine Corps informing him that Sergeant Dominic di Natale had been killed in an air accident over Cherry Point, North Carolina. It did not say that it had been Dominic's last day of flying or that he had been awaiting his release from service. If a man had been killed in action, there would have been glory. It was not right that Dominic should die like this.

The details would come later, but they were unimportant. Dominic had probably been taking too many chances that last day and all, and now his ship was crumpled in the sluggish waters of the Neuse River and his body was a thing to be gathered into a basket.

The priest wondered if Dominic's last look had been one of surprise. He rather thought it had. He would be so surprised to discover that his grandmother had been wrong about him and that he was not damned after all. Dominic had believed everybody.

It was better this way. He might have slipped again. Like

Bud Horne. No. Very different from Bud, but the same possible ending.

This ending was good. Now Dominic's portrait could hang over the high altar and his statue be erected with pride, and one could point to them both and not say, "He slipped again," but, "He died bravely. He made it."

Dominic and Dismas. Perhaps Christ knew best. Could Dismas have survived the long pull, the weariness of years, frustration, captivity? There were some people who needed a quick conversion and a promise that that day they would be in Paradise.

Better for Dominic than for Bill Martin. Than for Greeney.

Patiently Greeney had been waiting. He was not so efficient as Bud Horne had been and where Bud would intrude and make the priest get down to business, Greeney would just stand by and wait.

"What is it, Greeney?" the priest asked at last.

"I been trying to tell you. The warden wants you to call."

"Yes. I heard you say that."

"And you better look at those two tabs before you get him."

Idly the priest picked up the notes, but they, too, seemed relatively unimportant. One was from the bishop requesting that he come to see him as soon as possible, and the other was from the Department of Correction, saying that a commission was to be sent to Clinton Prison to investigate.

What did that matter? He remembered a similar day long ago when almost the same tabs had been lying there and he had been disturbed. Not now.

He would call the warden. See what this was about.

After the trying preliminaries the warden was saying, "I'm afraid this is a little beyond me, Padre. Did the best I could for you this time too. But they're sending a commission down on me, and I've got to be ready."

"Of course," the priest replied. "Is there anything I can do?"

"I'd advise you to get up to see your bishop as soon as you can. Get your case ready. This is pretty serious stuff. I'm afraid this is it."

"What is?"

"The charges against you."

"I don't get it. What are they saying I did? What charges?"

There was a perceptible pause from the warden's end of the wire. At last he spoke.

"Incitation to riot and assisting a prisoner to escape."

CHAPTER NINE

"The same thing happened to my predecessor," Father Hyland was saying to the bishop. "It is the pattern."

He had returned from Albany and he knew the exact extent of the charges. Incitation to riot, which meant that Bill Martin had not played the chimes that noontime when the bill had been vetoed; causing strike and disorder among the prison population—the same occasion; assisting jail break, which meant that he had purchased felt for a machine. These were the charges.

"Absurd," the bishop said.

"Yes. They are absurd. But they point to something. This one we can defeat. Then what's next?"

"I wouldn't worry," the bishop said kindly. "You are long overdue for a parish. I've been thinking about one for you." The bishop named the place.

Yes. Right now he could go out in a blaze of glory, to the kind of parish which one had no right to expect, even after many years of valiant service. He could take it, in case—in case he remembered Father Booth too strongly and what they had done to him.

"No, Your Excellency," he said slowly. "My sentence at Dannemora isn't over yet. I'm an old-timer, and they haven't cut down my years. And there's so much more to do!"

The bishop was amazed. "More? What more? What can be left to do?"

It would take a long time to tell the bishop. He could only outline it. There was the useless wall to remove so that men

268

could visit the church without going through four locked gates.
There was just the beginning of the social-service work for
inmates' relatives. There were plans for the group who would
volunteer to secure employment for parolees. There was the
work that he alone could do now with the inmates, which
would take years for another man to accomplish. It had taken
him years, hadn't it? And there was the religious order to be
established.

There were the men, his men. New men coming in all the
time.

"One thing more," the bishop said. "You haven't mentioned
that cinema of yours. Or is that a dead issue?"

"No, Your Excellency. We are going to have that—someday."

"You never give up, do you?"

Father Hyland smiled. "I just don't know when I'm licked."

"That's good," the bishop said. "And in a way I'm glad you
didn't leap at that parish. You weren't even tempted, were
you?"

"No, Bishop. I have the best parish in the world because it's
the worst."

The bishop rose now, imparting his blessing. "I'm very
proud of you. And as for these other matters—just ask that
commission from Albany to drop over and see me. I'm like
yourself, Father. I don't give up easily."

So he was right with the bishop, he thought, as he hurried
back to Dannemora. He was glad that the charges were so
extreme. They would fall of their own weight. And whoever
wanted his removal, for whatever purpose, would get nowhere. He would continue on his own course. Whatever they
did.

When he reached his little cottage he found trusties cutting
down the great trees that had protected him so long from the
view of the gates of Dannemora.

"Hey!" he called. "What are you doing?"

"Getting rid of the trees. Just got orders."

"Oh," he said. "I see."

With the trees down, the cottage would lie bare to the roadside and be totally visible from the turrets.

"In the future," he thought, "I'll have to pull the shades down."

He had never done that before in his life.

Let them look. He wouldn't do it now.

2. Mother Angela had written him:

We have crowned Our Lady with roses, a sweet custom, I think, and on this day we write some verses. Our littlest Sister wrote the enclosed. They do not scan very well, but at least they will prove that we are carrying on into the next generation, since they are on Saint Dismas.

The older I grow the more possibility I see for your men to live in their cells as we try to live in ours. You do teach them to love God. This was brought home to me very strongly yesterday.

One of your men came here. I could not see through the turn, of course, but he had a lovely, peaceful voice. He presented us with a panel of stained glass.

It was of Our Lady. I have never seen an auburn-haired Madonna before but it is quite beautiful, if touching. I know the man loved that picture. He said he wanted it here with us, because he couldn't have it. Does that mean anything to you? He said he was going to South America to work, and that you knew that, and would know why.

His name was Carlos and he kept calling Our Lady Mona.

Why don't you answer my letters?

Rigorous! Brother Anselm laughed. Everyone here lived to be a hundred. Sometimes he felt that he had never lived anywhere else but in this monastery, there was such a similarity between the life here and the life at Dannemora. Except for one thing. Here he had learned to pray.

He feared that he had never prayed before. Once he had thought that work interfered with prayer. Now he could pray better while he worked. If only he had known that, or had had that gift, through all those long years. How much good he could have done. It was hard to make up for it or to feel that he was doing penance when everything was so delightful.

Of course he had not had the grace then. He was only Max Bergner. Now he was Brother Anselm.

3. Although he had been exonerated of the strange charges that had been made against him, Father Hyland felt a sense of impermanency. Nothing had changed, but it was as if he were saying good-by. It had been so final that night at the conclusion of the mission when he had said, "Good night, Greeney, and Blackie and Brownie and Whitey. Good night, Bill and Jim and Joe and Jack. Good night, all of you. I shall never think of you as numbers. You will always be names to me." It had sounded like a valedictory.

That morning there had been something final about the way he had talked to Bill Martin. He had said, "You must stop worrying about Eddie. You had nothing to do with that. But you can pray for him. Offer your whole life for him. Nobody can take that power away from you. That can *be* your life. You have found a life here, Bill."

"Yes. I have found a life. Maybe it's better than it would have been outside. That's hard to say. But anyhow, I've done some things I wouldn't have done. Like this." He handed over a sheaf of music. "It's the Mass."

"Even the Agnus Dei?"

"Especially."

"After you heard about Eddie?" He saw Bill nod his head slowly. Was this the purpose of it all? Who could say? "Let me try it on the organ."

"Sure. In a minute. But before that—I just want to say I didn't, now, mean any harm about that signal on the chimes, Pops."

"Did I ever bawl you out about that, Bill?"

"No. That's the trouble. You always used to. For things like that. It's as if—as if——"

As if something were over. Ambrose Hyland knew.

So he went into the chancel and sat at the organ, playing softly at first, then louder, as the music came. He began the Agnus Dei as the voices started, and he realized that the whole choir, not vested as for Mass, but in prison gray, had come into their stalls, and were singing now while Martin led them. He smiled, for he fancied that Saint Dismas on the cross was listening, and the ear that was turned was not only for the voice of the Lord but also for these voices, as if Dominic in heaven were again surprised.

"Agnus Dei, qui tollis peccata mundi."

Take the sins of the world. Take from us everything we love. But You will not take the beauty that has been dedicated to You. Only the evil things out of our hearts. Our follies, our errors, our stupidities. But have mercy on us who have suffered with You, even to folly.

"Dona nobis pacem."

Grant us peace, all of us, and take the longing out of Carlos's heart and let him remember only that from his great love he has made these imperishable things. He had begotten beauty.

"Grant us peace!"

Peace. And a life here, important, and at rest. As You have given it to some of these—these lost, found sheep.

Tom Riordan was not quite ready for it yet but in a week or so, once the novena was over, Father Hyland said that he might do it. Now, sitting with the others in their heavy chairs around the sides of the room, he could forget the maunderings about him and remember the words.

"I, Thomas Riordan, in the presence of Almighty God, and with the help of Our Lady and of all the saints, and imploring the divine protection, do vow to accept all humiliations and ridicule which may come to me, and to seek for same, so long as it be not given me through malice of my neighbor, or through my own imprudence. These I offer unto the Divine Majesty first, in humble sorrow for my own sins, then for the sins of the world, and lastly that God in His infinite goodness may see fit to found a harbor of refuge for sinners and for criminals like myself."

In rehearsal, he said the words over and over again.

Then, at a command, all stood up, except one recalcitrant patient, and Tom Riordan went with the rest to the long white row of beds, where amid jeers he knelt for a little while and prayed.

4. Pops had changed. For weeks now Greeney had been in despair, trying to do the office work the way Bud Horne had done it. He did his best, but it was a poor best. He wished Pops would get a good secretary.

Then one day Pops hadn't cared whether things were just right or not. It was funny. Even when he had asked for these couple of days to work on his case, Pops had let him have them. Once he would have been mad. Not now.

He did have to work on his case, though. He had found out about a couple of lawyers in Boston, a Mr. and Mrs. Somebody, and how if he prayed for them to pass the bar they would take his case if they could get a new angle on it. They hadn't passed yet, and they didn't have a new angle, but they would.

Pops had only smiled and said, "Sure, Greeney, work on your case." Then he had said, "You never give up, do you, Greeney?"

"I can't," he replied. If he did, he would fall all to pieces.

"Neither can I. Go on and win, Greeney."

That was a funny one. He did not understand Pops these days. Oh well. He had to get down to his case.

The wild starling that he had taught to come to his cell, and whom he had trained to sing the first bars of "Home on the Range," came now and trilled at him. He would not notice him. He took out the old, soiled documents. He had creased and uncreased them so many times during the years.

"Don't sing, bird," he said. "Go away. I gotta work." He prayed, "Dear God, you gotta help me, see? I'm innocent. I didn't do what they said I did. So You gotta help me."

He knew God would.

"Go away, old bird. Old jailbird." The bird would not go. Greeney went on working on his case.

5. In the evening Ambrose Hyland came down the hill after a strenuous day, and a strange thought struck him. There below, as he waited for the guard to release him, resting his two bags for a moment, he saw a knot of men on an incoming draft, huddled together at the gates of Dannemora.

Suppose now that he were outside the gate, a young priest, looking in at those men. What would he be thinking?

Fifteen years ago, waiting there, coming to this place where he was a stranger. Soon, inevitably, a young priest must come here. What would he think, standing at the gates?

He would think: All those years Hyland has been here and he hasn't got that wall down yet. What was the matter with him? Gadding all over the country on movies that never materialized.

Then the gates would open and he would study the situation a little. At first the men would be hostile, because the rumor would have spread that he had been in back of the charges of incitation to riot, fomenting strikes, assisting a prison break. But he would soon discover what was the matter.

"It's obvious," he would say. "What these men need is a hope, once they get out of here. We've got to have places for them to go. Why didn't the old man go to work on that?"

The young priest would come up to the distant parish and he would find out what mistakes he had made and set him right. Then he would say in answer to the young priest's enthusiasms, "Well, we did get a little start on that. You'll find letters in the files from the Buckley Brothers. They made a beginning at getting jobs for parolees."

"How many?"

"One, so far. They think they can get more. I thought, if we could interest some other men in that work, we might be going in the right direction. I thought it might be the beginning of the League of Our Lady of Ransom."

Then the young priest, full of zeal, would look at him pityingly.

"It'll have to be bigger than that."

Yes. He knew. It would have to be bigger than that.

Joe Hogan had been a long time opening the gate, but now he came. "You're looking fine tonight, Padre."

Good Lord, the priest thought, they never said things like that to you until you began to grow old. Why shouldn't he look fine? There was no change in him since he came here, except a pound or two and five gray hairs over each ear. What was the idea? How long since they had begun to call him Pops? Why, just the other day he had become only fifty. What was the matter with these youngsters?

"I don't see how you stand it," Joe Hogan went on. "You go the same pace every day. The thing that gets me is they haven't got you institutionalized. That's better than I can say for myself. To me, now, they're just numbers. What's your secret? And say—how long you been here anyway?"

"Fifteen years," Father Hyland replied. "Only fifteen years so far."

Then they were at the outer gate and in a moment he was within the far enclosure where the draft stood. Again he waited, scanning the faces of these new men who would not be numbers, but his sheep—his black sheep. There was one in particular, a red-blond lad who had an undefeated alertness about him. He could use him in the office—if it wouldn't break Greeney's heart. Must keep his eye on him. Must keep his eye on all of them, always.

He saw them coming like this, like waves, dark waves against a coast, tossed here on this rock, drawn back into the places under the sea, eternities of men, great multitudes of them, while he stood like Canute, forbidding the tides. He saw the vastness of human dereliction and of the inscrutable powers that moved mankind, the currents of good and evil, the vortexes, the whirlpools. Who was to control that inundation of evil?

Who was he, or a thousand like him? Who was the young man who would come here to replace him? He could as soon have stopped the surges of the ocean as he could the horrors of the world outside that had brought these men to be here for a little while where there was haven and peace.

That was enough. Enough for one lifetime. Enough for his own life.

"Grant us peace." Once again he could hear the prison choir singing as the light fell from the stained-glass windows upon them, the windows set with the faces of horror and of glory, and Dismas looking down. This was what he had always fancied as the conclusion of the great drama which might never be flashed upon the screen. But he had seen it ending thus.

For a long time Brendon O'Malley had been kept waiting. He had watched while a black-cloaked figure had stood at the upper gate. He had followed, with his eyes, the path down which the priest had come, and he saw a church rising incongruously above the fortressed hillside. He counted the gates that lay between. Four gates. Four gates to Dannemora.

Then the priest had entered the enclosure and for a moment had scanned the crowd. After that he stood, looking upward at the reflected sunlight behind the church. The wind made folds in his garments. His strong, carven profile was against the sky. In him was the look of youth, of one with a vision, of one never to be defeated.

It was as if a voice spoke to Brendon, "This is my man. I will know him. He is sure and certain as I have never been. I will find him and work with him. I will see the things he is seeing."

Then the guard spoke, and the line of men proceeded through the first gate, and Brendon O'Malley, convict, began life at Clinton Prison, Dannemora, New York.

The others followed.

And Brendon thought, "We will see what he sees."

What he saw was this.

The contrasts of that countryside, the vast Adirondacks spreading out in a wild rapture to the skies, and this barred, narrowed place, enclosed within the gates of hell. The terrible hillside that they called the Big Yard, unspeakably ugly, cut off by a huge wall from the lovely gardened hill that was the chapel enclosure. The church, beautiful in pointing and towering loveliness, surmounting the red-brick horror of cell upon cell, tier upon tier, sorrow upon sorrow. The clean smell of the air upon the hill; the thick odors from the factory below, like heaven and hell.

Then, as he saw it, the camera would sweep within the church and the choir would be singing, and Dismas—Dominic —upon the cross would hear a voice, and his head would rise still more, and he would look up into the opening heavens, while freedom would be like a pain about him, freedom would be like love, and the great Voice would follow, saying to a thief the greatest words ever spoken by God to the human race, "This day thou shalt be with Me in Paradise."

And Father Ambrose Hyland took up his two black bags and went on. The greatest of the four gates clanged behind him. He turned left toward the State Hospital, to receive Tom Riordan's vows.